A Magna Colour Guide

Poisonous Plants

A Magna Colour Guide

Poisonous Plants

by František Starý

Illustrated by

Zdeněk Berger

MAGNA
BOOKS

581.6

S

Editor's Note

While this is primarily a valuable reference work on poisonous plants, it will also have the added benefit of pointing out to the reader the obvious dangers of such plants as, of course, prevention is better than cure.

Text by František Starý
Illustrations by Zdeněk Berger
Translated by Olga Kuthanová
Graphic design by Eva Adamcová

This edition published 1995 by
Magna Books
Magna Road, Wigston,
Leicester LE18 4ZH
and produced in co-operation with
Arcturus Publishing Limited

Copyright © 1990 Aventinum, Prague
First published 1983 by Artia, Prague

ISBN 1 85422 834 X
Printed in Slovakia by Neografia, Martin
3/15/09/51-02

CONTENTS

INTRODUCTION

'Alle Dinge sind Gift und
nichts ist ohne Gift.
Allein die Dosis macht, dass
ein Ding kein Gift ist.'
  Paracelsus (1493—1541)

'All things are poison and
nothing is without poison.
The dose alone decides
that a thing is not poison.'
  Paracelsus (1493—1541)

The definition by Paracelsus needs no qualification; it remains valid
to this day. Poison is a relative term, because every poison may, in
a certain dose, be a medicine, and a so-called harmless substance may
become a poison. This definition applies in toxicology, a relatively
new science dealing with poisons and their effects on the human and
animal system. Even though human and veterinary toxicology differ
in terms of the object of their study, the subject of both — poisons
and their effects — has much in common.

Modern science defines poison as follows: a poison is any substance which by its chemical composition, under certain conditions
and in a certain quantity and form may affect one or more organs of
the animal and human system in such a manner as to seriously damage the health, temporarily or permanently, and even to cause death.
The term 'substance' includes organic as well as inorganic compounds, synthetic as well as natural. A poison, then, is not only a substance that causes death, but also a substance that seriously affects
the health, be it only temporarily.

From the medical viewpoint, a poison is generally considered to be
a substance which, when it enters the human system even if only in
a relatively small quantity and when absorbed, causes pathological
changes that may result in death.

From the legal viewpoint, a poison is any substance that causes
changes in the chemical composition and function of a living cell. This
legal definition is the basis for the laws that must be observed in the
production, distribution, sale and handling of poisons. For example, in
a pharmacy where most of the medicinal substances *(materia medica)*
may be classed as poisonous substances, they are divided into *materia
medica separanda* and *materia medica seclusa.* Separanda are relatively mild poisons stored in containers marked with red lettering on
white. They include, for example, the alkaloids codeine, caffeine and
theobromine and the inorganic salts of heavy metals — copper sulphate, zinc sulphate etc. Seclusa are extremely virulent poisons stored
in containers marked with black lettering on white and kept separate
from other medicinal substances in a locked cupboard. They include,

for example, the alkaloids hyoscyamine, atropine, scopolamine and strychnine and of the anorganic substances certain mercury compounds (sublimates), arsenic compounds, cyanides and the like.

Poisons are marked with a warning sign — the international symbol of a skull and cross-bones — and the inscription **'POISON'**, in whatever language.

The scientific nomenclature of the taxons in this book is according to the eleventh edition of the handbook *'Zander Handwörterbuch der Pflanzennamen'* (Stuttgart, Eug. Ulmer Verl., 1979). The text accompanying each colour plate contains data from contemporary (up to the year 1981) world literature on botany, pharmaceutical chemistry and toxicology.

POISONS IN NATURE

Poisons in nature occur not only in plants but also in minerals containing mostly heavy metals. The latter cause chronic poisoning in, for example, miners and smelters; they include, for instance, lead, zinc, mercury, bismuth, arsenic, phosphorus and their compounds. Halogens (chlorine, iodine, bromine, fluorine), with their strong corrosive and irritant action, are also dangerously toxic. Likewise, certain gases produced by chemical reactions in nature may be fatal to living organisms; these include carbon dioxide, carbon monoxide, hydrogen sulphide, carbon disulphide and hydrogen cyanide.

The animal kingdom also includes a number of poisonous species, or rather species that produce poisonous substances for killing prey or for purposes of defence. Best known of these are the snake venoms. Of the approximately 1500 species of snakes, some 900 are poisonous. Certain fish and amphibians, e.g. salamanders and frogs, are

Skull and cross-bones
— an emblem of death
used as a danger sign.

poisonous too. There are few poisonous species among the coelenterates, worms, molluscs and echinoderms, but in the large phylum of arthropods, which has the most species in the animal kingdom (nine-tenths of all existing species), are the poisonous scorpions, centipedes, spiders, and insects such as the many poisonous species of beetles, lepidopteran larvae and hymenopterans.

Only an approximate calculation can be made at the moment as to the number of poisonous in relation to non-poisonous plants. About one-third of the total number of plant species produces poisonous substances, but these are not always dangerous. Oxalic acid, for example, is a relatively strong poison for man: even 5 gm is a fatal dose, as is 20 gm of the soluble salts of this acid. Numerous plants contain fairly large amounts of oxalic acid and yet they are generally not thought of as poisonous plants (e.g. plants of the genus *Rumex* L. or sorrel and of the genus *Chenopodium* L. or goosefoot). It is known, however, that after grazing in neglected pasture with a great abundance of these species horses, sheep and cattle exhibit symptoms of poisoning. Probably no one would say that such fruits as strawberries, apricots and peaches were poisonous; however, if eaten in large quantities they may cause allergic reactions in some people, particularly children, accompanied by skin rashes and digestive disorders. These are brought about by the organic acids and also the aromatic substances in the fruits. The same is true of herbs and spices. They, too, cannot be said to be poisonous but if consumed in excess they may have unpleasant effects. People do not all have the same degree of tolerance towards certain herbs, however. Kidney damage has been known to result from excessive use of parsley root, lovage root and celeriac. Symptoms of poisoning have been recorded also resulting from the use of too much paprika and pepper in foods. Also dangerous if used in large amounts is such popular seasoning as chili powder and curry powder (a powder made from turmeric, ginger, cardamom and various other spices and herbs). These examples show the truth of Paracelsus's quotation printed at the beginning of this book.

POISONS ARE NOT POISONOUS FOR ALL

There are many examples of plant substances that are poisonous for man but not for other animals and vice versa. The berries of Yew (see *Taxus baccata*) have a non-toxic fleshy aril but very poisonous seeds. Birds feed on the fruit, including the seeds, without harm. The seeds pass through the birds' digestive system without any toxic effect and are distributed in their droppings. Birds also feed on the fruit of Mezereon (see *Daphne mezereum*) without harm.

The Colorado Beetle is capable of multiplying on Deadly Nightshade (see *Atropa bella-donna*). Its larvae feed on the leaves, which contain extremely poisonous tropane alkaloids. These alkaloids may even be analytically identified in the larvae. However, they do not hinder the development of the larvae and in congenial conditions the Colorado Beetle may produce as many as three generations on Deadly Nightshade.

The Silkworms *(Attacus ricini)* cultivated in Assam feed only on the leaves of the Castor-oil Plant (see *Ricinus communis*), which contain the poisonous alkaloid ricinine.

It is known that bees visit poisonous plants too. Although the poisonous substances are often found in the flowers, they have no effect on the bees. However, the honey from such flowers may be poisonous for man, e.g. honey from Oleander (see *Nerium oleander*), Rusty-leaved Rhododendron (see *Rhododendron ferrugineum*) and Wild Rosemary (see *Ledum palustre*).

Goats may feed on belladonna without any ill-effects if they consume a small quantity, but their milk and, immediately after grazing, their meat are poisonous.

After white-haired animals, such as goats, have fed on certain species of plants and then been out in the sun, they exhibit photosensitive symptoms in the form of inflammatory eruptions in areas not covered by hair, e.g. round the ears, eyes and mouth. Photosensitivity is caused by, for example, St John's Wort and Tartarian Buckwheat. Similar symptoms, often very painful and dangerous, are caused in man by plants containing furocoumarins, e.g. plants of the parsley (Umbelliferae) family. False Bishop's Weed *(Ammi majus L.)* appears to be the most dangerous to man. Animals are generally not sensitive to furocoumarin-type substances.

Pyrethrins, organic substances found in Pyrethrum *(Chrysanthemum cinerariaefolium* [Trev.] Vis.*)* are highly poisonous to all insects on contact whereas they are not poisonous to warm-blooded animals and man. For this reason they are used successfully as insecticides in fields, warehouses and the home. The importance of these substances is highlighted also by the scientific prize awarded by UNESCO in 1978 for the synthesis of pyrethroids, which should gradually replace insecticides based on chlorinated compounds (DDT) or organophosphates (Parathion, etc.) that have proved damaging to plant and animal life.

A BRIEF LOOK AT THE HISTORY OF POISONS AND THEIR ABUSE

The main abuses of poisons are: in premeditated murder; in trying to cause a state of mental breakdown in another human being, and in suicide. Religious ecstasy accompanied by ritual ceremonies where poisons are used to produce hallucinations is another form of abuse as is narcotism, the addiction to narcotic drugs.

In ancient times, poisons were a requisite of many rulers and their entourage in their struggle for power. Poisons were doubtless used by ordinary people too but little was written about that. Much has been recorded about poisons and antidotes. For instance, in the second century B.C., the Greek physician and poet Nicander of Colophon wrote instructive poems on antidotes for the bite of venomous snakes (which he called *Theriaka*) and on antidotes for poisons (which he called *Alexifarmaka*). From this it is evident that the terms poison and medicament must have been known for centuries. The question is which came first and which was given precedence; from the pages of history the conclusion is that it was poison. Rulers who used poison to rid themselves of their enemies included e. g. Clearchus (circa 400 B. C.), the Spartan general, and Dionysius I. (406—367 B.C.), the Tyrant of ancient Syracuse. The Roman Emperor Nero (A.D. 37–68) had the son of Emperor Claudius Britannicus poisoned. Emperor Vespasian (A. D. 9—79), his son Titus (A. D. 38—81) and Titus's brother Domitian (A. D. 51—96), who were also Roman emperors, were all poisoned. Emperor Commodus was poisoned too, in A. D. 192, by his mistress in league with conspirators. These are only a few examples of murder by poisoning in ancient times. In those days, the death sentence could be carried out by forced suicide, as in the case of Socrates, the Greek philosopher (469—399 B. C.) who was condemned to death by the drinking of Hemlock (see *Conium maculatum*). Collecting poisons was also a fashion of the time and one of the most famous collections was that of Caracalla (A. D. 188—217), Roman Emperor from A. D. 211 to 217.

The mighty of this world had their enemies poisoned and were often exposed to the same danger themselves. They therefore engaged court tasters whose function was not only to test the quality of their master's food and drink but also to detect poisoning, to act as a human filter or obstacle to any attempt at murder by poison. The poisons selected for the purpose were ones with a rapid action and plant poisons played an important role.

The fourteenth to sixteenth centuries in Europe were a veritable

Poison rings.

paradise for professional poisoners. In Italy and France in particular this was an inauspicious but lucrative profession. In the annals of Italian poisoners there are whole families who were masters of this 'trade', for example the Visconti della Scala, the Baglioni and the Borgia families. Catherine de Medici was considered to be one of the greatest poisoners in history. She solved complicated political problems by using poison, spilling it into the cup of adversaries.

In France, too, poisoning was one of the methods of settling accounts besides the traditional duel. As in Italy, women headed the list: the Marquise de Montespan; Jeanne Stanulin called Chausée, and the professional poisoner 'La Voisine', who rid nobles of their burdensome mistresses during the reign of Louis XIV.

Poison rings were a common requisite of this medieval period. They could be worn without attracting notice for the fashion of the time favoured the wearing of jewels of all kinds. Poison rings had a lid decorated with a cameo, precious stone or enamel, beneath which was a skilfully concealed space containing the poison. It was not at all difficult, given an opportune moment, to empty the poison from the ring into a cup of wine or to swallow it. The ring's owner

Receptacle for poisons.

could either poison somebody else or he might take his own life rather than face a sentence or torture. Poisons were also frequently kept in richly decorated receptacles, often of great artistic value. Decorated flacons, similar to those for holding perfume, were widely used by women for this purpose.

Poison receptacles were also cleverly concealed in necklaces. Modern receptacles include such items as poison teeth, where the poison in a glass micro-ampoule is concealed in a cavity beneath a removable crown, and special dentures with a mechanism for releasing poison. These are precious requisites of persons contemplating the possible use of poison to avoid a prison sentence or dreaded interrogation.

Poisons that do not kill but in certain, measured doses produce a state of stupor are a group apart. Scopolamine, for instance, is used as a means of eliciting information that could not be obtained under normal circumstances. The information may not be entirely accurate for under the influence of the drug (scopolamine) a person talks of his hidden thoughts and desires without their necessarily having taken place. He may, for example, confess to murders he never committed. A small quantity of scopolamine or cocaine in a glass of wine can even make a person agree to engage in sexual intercourse.

In the Middle Ages, poisonous plants from the Solanaceae family (see *Atropa bella-donna, Hyoscyamus niger, Scopolia carniolica*) were used to produce hallucinations and cause flights into the 'world of spirits — primarily the world of demons'. It was mostly women who took part in such orgies. Extracts from the plants mentioned were generally applied in the form of concentrated ointments to the mucous membrane of the genitals. The action of the tropane alkaloids, principally scopolamine, produced colourful hallucinations of a sexual nature. These hallucinations often included demons and occasionally saints — in short, the fantasies of medieval man, bound by religion and superstition. The hallucinations often took on the guise of motion, such as riding on a broomstick. 'Flights to witches' sabbaths' were often group events. The Inquisition meted out punishment in the form of death by burning for such 'witches'. This was in fact narcotic addiction similar to that of the present day but marked by the medieval period and by the generally miserable life of the common people.

Drug addiction is the habitual use of narcotics (poisons) for the purpose of attaining a pleasant feeling of well-being, an escape from the often unpleasant reality of everyday life. The repeated evoking of these pleasant sensations leads to dependence on and addiction to the respective poison, the endeavour to obtain the drug by whatever means, and the use of increasing amounts in the belief that more will produce even better effects. Usually, the fact that the original, small doses no longer produce the expected sensations is not noticed. Man apparently has a tendency to drug addiction and that is why nowadays there are so many people throughout the world who have become victims of this habit.

The definition of narcotic addiction is that it is a condition of periodic or chronic poisoning that is harmful to both the individual and society. It is caused by the habitual use of narcotic drugs of natural origin or synthetic or semi-synthetic substances. The most widespread is morphinism, addiction to the morphine component of opium alkaloids (see *Papaver somniferum*) or to semi-synthetic morphine derivatives. Opium itself is rarely taken in its pure form *per os,* that is by the mouth in pills or tinctures; it is generally smoked, a wide variety of

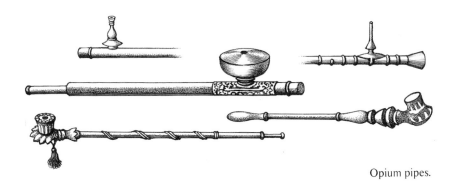

Opium pipes.

13

Various receptacles for coca leaves.

ornamental pipes of diverse shape being used, mostly wooden, bamboo or water pipes.

The hashish addiction of the Orient, chiefly India, and the smoking of marihuana are likewise grave problems that pose a serious threat to society.

A common and widespread addiction in the Arab states is cathaism, chewing of the leaves, young twigs and shoots of the shrub *Catha edulis* Forsk. of the Celastraceae family. In time, this damages the digestive system, causing ulcers and general deterioration of the organism.

In the New World, the most widespread addiction is cocainism, the habitual use of cocaine, which is obtained by chewing the leaves of coca (see *Erythroxylum coca*). Peyotl or mescal (see *Lophophora williamsii*) is another of the many addictive drugs of Mexico and Central and South America.

The area where betel nut is chewed (see *Piper betle*) is immense and 200 million people are addicted to this drug.

Smoking tobacco (see *Nicotiana tabacum*), drinking coffee and tea and even cocoa are no longer viewed as addictive although smoking still is in the true meaning of the term.

Modern science has also come up with new drugs that lend themselves to addiction. The synthesis of lysergic acid diethylamid (LSD), for example, has become a dangerous hallucinogenic, addictive drug. It is a derivative of lysergic acid, basic component in the biosynthesis of ergot alkaloids found in ergot, *Claviceps purpurea* (Fries) Tul., a parasitic fungus of grasses, growing chiefly on rye. Similar effects are produced also by other alkaloids obtained from fungi, e.g. psilocybine and psilocine.

14

COLOUR ILLUSTRATIONS

Crab's Eye, Rosary Pea
Abrus precatorius L.

Leguminosae

The genus *Abrus* Adans. has only four species distributed throughout the world. *A. precatorius* is a tropical species. It is often grown for its strikingly coloured seeds, which are extremely poisonous. They contain a poisonous protein, the phytotoxin abrin, one of the most toxic plant substances of all. Swallowing a single, well-chewed seed may be fatal to man. The symptoms of poisoning are stomach pains, followed by vomiting, collapse, a state of coma and death. Cattle and goats are more immune, but 60 — 120 gm of seeds may kill a horse. In India and Sri Lanka, domestic animals have been successfully immunized with subcutaneous injections of minimal non-toxic doses of abrin.

In medicine, abrin has been tested for its effect on cancerous, tumour cells in animals. Sublethal doses destroyed the tumours but it has been impossible to use abrin with safety in the fight against cancer because of its extreme toxicity. It is often used, however, to evil ends — premeditated murder, chiefly in India. The instrument of death is the seed itself, which while still soft is shaped into a sharp point. A stab with such a 'weapon' is generally fatal for when abrin enters the bloodstream directly its action is even more aggressive than when it passes through the digestive tract. The east African species *A. schimperi* is used by the natives as an antidote for scorpion bites.

Abrus precatorius is a shrub with vine-like branches up to 5 m long and covered with adpressed hairs. The leaves are odd-pinnate, with 8 — 15 paired leaflets; the individual leaflets are elliptical, 1.5 by 0.5 cm, and almost sessile. The median vein terminates in a spine extending beyond the blunt edge of the blade. The hermaphrodite flowers, coloured red, pink and occasionally white, are arranged in thick, axial racemes. The calyx is funnel-shaped with short lobes, the corolla consists of an ovate-lanceolate standard, narrow wings and twisted keel. The stamens are fused. The fruit (1a) is a longish flat pod splitting along two sutures with the seeds in separate 'compartments' (1b). The seeds remain attached, as if stuck, to the pod long after it has split. They are scarlet with a black patch round the micropyle, 6 — 7 mm long and 4 — 5 mm wide, plump, ellipsoid, smooth, glossy and

1b

hard (2). They have long been used in making ornaments. In Central America and the Caribbean region, they are used to make beads and necklaces as well as rosaries.

16

2

1a

17

Common Monkshood, Aconite
Aconitum napellus L.

The number of species in the genus *Aconitum* L. is estimated at 280—300 and they are found in mountain districts in the northern hemisphere. Many have lovely flowers, both in shape and colour, and many are grown for garden decoration. All the plant organs contain poisonous alkaloids, principally aconitine, in amounts of 1—3 per cent. These are chiefly concentrated in the tubers and are among the most violent poisons of the plant kingdom. The fatal dose for man is 3—8 mg. Cases of poisoning are not common in western Europe because it is widely known that aconites are poisonous. The only cases on record are ones where the victims were children. Luckily, the tubers, which are the most poisonous, are deep in the ground and thus not easy to get at. Poisoning is common in veterinary medicine, however, chiefly in cattle, sheep and goats fed fodder containing aconite. When put out to graze, the animals are careful to avoid aconite. Least affected are horses. Symptoms of poisoning in man are a tingling feeling in the mouth, which soon spreads to the whole face and is followed by chills, sweating, vomiting, great fatigue and a feeling of anxiety. Death occurs due to respiratory failure and heart damage, with the victim fully conscious. Because of its great toxicity, aconitine extracted from the tubers is used only occasionally in European medicine in minimal therapeutic doses for the treatment of certain cases of severe neuralgia, including trigeminal neuralgia. It is used more widely in east Asian phytotherapy. The one-time use of aconite to poison captives is a thing of the past, as is its use for poisoning arrows in India.

The most widely known species is *Aconitum napellus* L., which flowers from July until September. It is an attractive plant, up to 1.5 m high, with flowers that are striking in both colour and shape arranged in racemes with bracts. The helmet is not the corolla but the blue calyx (1). The corolla is modified into nectaries concealed deep inside the helmet. The black seeds, with sharp to winged edges, are in three follicles (2) of 10—15 seeds each. Typical are the underground tubers. The old tuber dies at the end of the growing season and the new, daughter tuber serves as the food store for the following season. The flowers of most aconites are coloured

3

1

2

various shades of blue or yellow and
there are many different shapes, e.g. the
yellow-flowering European species
A. lycoctonum L. (3) with high-domed
helmet.

Common Baneberry
Actaea spicata L.

The genus *Actaea* L., with seven species, is distributed throughout the northern hemisphere. Best known is the Euro-Siberian species. *A. spicata* found in the northerly parts of Europe (in the south only in mountain districts) and in the arctic and temperate regions of Asia. In Europe, it grows in the beech woods and mixed broad-leaved woods of the mountain belt.

Its toxicity is generally ascribed to protoanemonine derived from the glycoside ranunculin, which is commonly found in plants of this family. Externally, baneberry causes skin rashes and blisters. Internally, particularly after ingestion of berries, it causes vomiting, diarrhoea, unpleasant inflammations of the digestive organs, stupor and delirium. American toxicological literature states that abdominal pains and cardiac weakness ensue on eating six berries. This applies chiefly to the species *A. alba* (L.) Mill. and *A. rubra* (Ait.) Willd., which are common and widespread in the woodlands of eastern North America. Poisoning is usually not fatal but convalescence is lengthy. There is no record of animals being poisoned for they are repelled by the plant's odour. Formerly, the roots and top parts were used in medicine as a drug for the preparation of tinctures, and extracts were prescribed for the treatment of neuralgia and rheumatic pains. Frequent and unintentional overdoses led to poisoning and for that reason the vegetable drug was eliminated from therapy. However, the fresh plant roots continue to be used for making medicaments employed in homeopathy.

A perennial up to 70 cm high with an unpleasant foetid smell, Common Baneberry has a thick knotty blackish-brown rhizome and an erect little-branched stem covered with alternate stalked pinnate leaves. The hermaphrodite flowers, arranged in multi-flowered racemes, are produced in early summer. The sepals are white, tipped with violet and fall off early. The petals are modified into linear white sterile nectaries. There is a large number of stamens. The ovary is pear-shaped (1). The fruit is a glossy black, many-seeded berry (2). The berries of cultivated garden varieties may also be red or white. The numerous seeds are semi-globose and brown. Members of the genus *Actaea* are

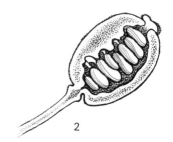

2

morphologically very similar to and have the same distribution as plants of the genus *Cimicifuga* Wernischek (Ranunculaceae). They also are poisonous and cause similar symptoms of poisoning.

1

Pheasant's Eye
Adonis annua L. emend. Huds.

The annual species of the genus *Adonis* L., native to the Middle East, occur as weeds among cereal crops and herbaceous grasses in the warm, lowland districts of Europe and Asia. The flowers are attractively coloured but small and, unlike their perennial counterparts, are not chosen for garden decoration.

    A. annua and other annual species such as Summer Pheasant's Eye (*A. aestivalis* L.) and Scarlet Pheasant's Eye (*A. flammea* Jacq.) contain poisonous glycosides; the most violent are adonitoxin and strophanthin glycosides (see also *Strophanthus hispidus*). They have a specific stimulant effect on the action of the heart muscle. Cases of poisoning are few and far between; those on record were the result of improper dosage in folk medicine where the drug was used in the form of an infusion (tea) as a remedy for dropsy. Excessive dosage caused retching accompanied by thirst and a feeling of weakness. There is no record of fatalities. For animals, the annual species of adonis are not particularly dangerous because the concentration of poisonous glycosides is relatively low. Nevertheless, poisoning of poultry and the young of domestic animals has been recorded in the less-developed parts of Asia caused by the feeding of cereal grasses greatly contaminated by the achenes of these weedy plants. Similarly, grasses such as clover and alfalfa with a greater proportion of Summer Pheasant's Eye (*A. aestivalis*) may produce symptoms of poisoning in calves or kids. These are usually mild cases of poisoning lasting only a short while. In medicine, annual species of adonis are hardly used at all because of the low concentration of active principles.

Annual, summer-flowering species of adonis are slender herbaceous plants approximately 50 cm high and usually only thinly leaved. The leaves are fine and thread-like. The flowers are regular with up to eight petals that are red with a dark blotch at the base, the colouring ranging from brick-red to carmine. Summer Pheasant's Eye is distinguished by its vermilion petals (1). Very occasionally one may come across its lemon-yellow form (forma *citrina*). The

1

2

fruits are hard, indehiscent achenes with characteristic beaks (2) that develop clustered together on the conical receptacle after pollination and fertilization.

23

Spring Pheasant's Eye
Adonis vernalis L.

Ranunculaceae

Perennial plants of this genus (10—15 species) grow in Europe and Asia, the best known being Spring Pheasant's Eye. It is a typical spring-flowering plant of the steppe and among Pubescent Oaks, chiefly on limestone substrates. It is distributed throughout the steppe regions of Europe but occurs mostly in the Asian countries of the former U.S.S.R. The lovely, large, golden-yellow flowers have made it a popular rock garden plant and it is widely grown for decoration.

Spring Pheasant's Eye and other perennial species contain poisonous glycosides, e.g. adonitoxin, adonitoxol, k-strophantidin, vernadigin and acetyl-adonitoxin, which first and foremost affect the action of the heart. In small quantities they have a stimulating effect, but in excessively large doses they cause serious, often irreparable heart damage. Cases of human poisoning are rare. European folk medicine almost never made use of this plant. It was not until the mid-nineteenth century that Spring Pheasant's Eye was used in therapy in the form of tea made from the dried flowering top parts. Only later were the separate glycosides recovered from the crude drug. Cases of livestock poisoning are also uncommon because the animals find the burning, bitter taste of the plant unpleasant and avoid it when grazing. Nevertheless, cases of poisoning of young animals have been recorded. The symptoms are abdominal pains and diarrhoea and finally cardiac arrest. Most readily affected are colts, kids and ducks; cattle are least susceptible.

2

Spring Pheasant's Eye is a perennial herb that puts out new growth in early spring (April — May) from the blackish brown rhizome deep in the soil. The flowering as well as leafy stems are scaly at the base and about 20—30 cm high. The leaves are two- or three-pinnate and thread-like. The flowers are large, up to 8 cm across, with 10—20 petals and a large number of stamens. The fruits are beaked

achenes (1) forming a dense cluster that disintegrates before the fruits are fully ripe.

Other related species are also grown in the rock garden, primarily *A. amurensis* Regel et Radde (2) from the Far East and *A. volgensis* Stev. These, however, are not as attractive as Spring Pheasant's Eye but they flower about a month earlier (in March — April).

Fool's Parsley
Aethusa cynapium L.

Umbelliferae

The genus *Aethusa* L. has only one species with a Euro-Siberian distribution. In Europe, it extends from the middle regions northward. It also occurs in Algeria and North America, where it is not indigenous but was introduced. It is a widespread, common weed of cultivated ground, parks and gardens.

The plant's toxicity is probably due to the organic compounds called polyines or polyacetylenes. Pharmacologically little is known about them as yet because isolation of these compounds is difficult due to their instability; they are, however, the substances that make not only this but also other species of this family poisonous. Some authorities believe that the causes of the plant's toxicity are coniine alkaloids such as cynapine. The essential oil containing these alkaloids, found chiefly in the fruits, has an unpleasant smell but is not poisonous.

The symptoms of poisoning are the same as from Hemlock (see *Conium maculatum*) but far milder: first of all, a state of excitement, which gradually changes to depression accompanied by paralysis of the skeletal muscles, vomiting and diarrhoea. The pupils are dilated; death is caused by suffocation with the heart action remaining normal. Fatal cases of human poisoning have occurred when the leaves of Fool's Parsley were mistaken for those of parsley *(Petroselinum)*. Serious cases of poisoning are not common in animals. Fool's Parsley is little used in folk medicine. The fresh juice from the top parts was formerly used, with risk, to dissolve uroliths and gravel. Homeopathy also uses the fresh top parts in minute quantities for similar problems.

This is a typical annual and in warm regions overwintering herb of the parsley family. It reaches a height of more than 1 m, particularly in cultivated soil. The stem is hollow, angled and tinged with violet. The flowers, in many-flowered umbels, are white and are produced from June until October. The fruits (1a) are schizocarpic double achenes, nearly globose, convex with five prominent ribs on the upper side and flat on the underside. The darker markings between the ribs are the ducts containing essential oil (1b). The young stems and leaves may be easily mistaken for those of parsley (2), particularly where Fool's Parsley occurs as a weed in beds of cultivated parsley. The former, however, is distinguishable from the cultivated kitchen herb by its repulsive smell.

1b

1a

2

27

Corn Cockle
Agrostemma githago L.

Caryophyllaceae

The weedy character of its members is indicated already by the scientific name of this genus, one with very few species. The name *Agrostemma* is derived from the Greek words *agros,* meaning field, and *stemma,* meaning wreath — in the figurative sense a plant that adorns fields. Corn Cockle spread to practically all the grain-growing regions of the world with the grain in which it occurred, most often as a weed. It is thought to have its origins in the Middle East. Corn Cockle seeds have been discovered in archeological excavations dating from the Neolithic period.

The poisonous substance in this plant is the saponin glycoside githagin, found primarily in the ripe seeds (4 — 7 per cent). The other parts of the plant, including the roots, contain only trace quantities. The saponin character of githagin causes haemolysis, the destruction of red corpuscles. This is accompanied by abdominal pains, diarrhoea and inflammation of the digestive tract. The central nervous system is also affected. Fatal cases end in cardiac arrest and respiratory failure. Feeding grain with an admixture of the seed to animals may cause poisoning in horses and other domestic animals. It is interesting to note that poultry is relatively immune to poisoning by Corn Cockle seeds. Carnivores are much more susceptible than herbivores. Today, such poisoning no longer occurs in Europe due to the modern methods of cleaning grain, and Corn Cockle is gradually disappearing from the countryside. The poisonous saponin has no use in medicine. Only homeopathy uses the extract from the seeds for treating gastritis and inflammation of the urinary passages. In folk medicine Corn Cockle was used as a diuretic and anthelmintic agent.

Corn Cockle is an annual felted herb with stems sparsely covered with narrow opposite leaves. The violet-red flowers, borne singly at the tips of the stems, are five-petalled. Extending between and beyond the petals are the narrow, linear sepals. The ovary is superior and unilocular. The fruit is a hard, dry, longish-ovoid capsule (1a) containing up to 40 kidney-shaped seeds measuring about 3.5 by 3 mm (1b). They are matt and covered with concentric rings of small tubercles (2). A single plant may produce as many as 300 seeds but the capsule does not open spontaneously when ripe and the seeds usually remain inside until they are released by threshing; that is why Corn Cockle has practically disappeared from some regions.

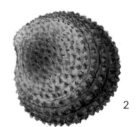

2

28

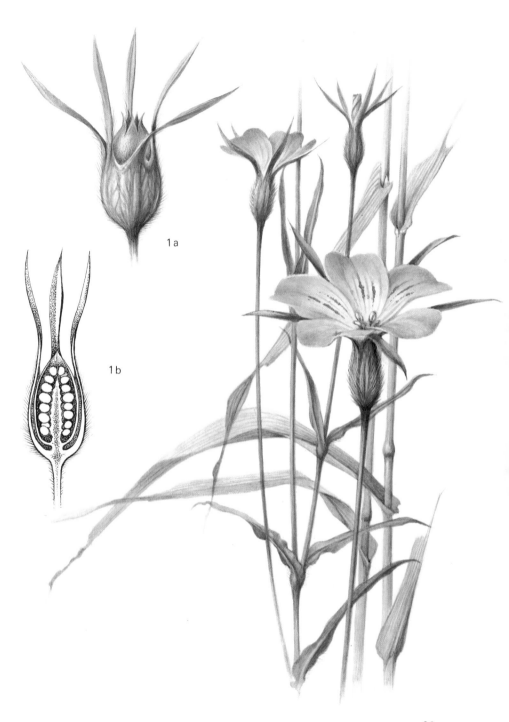

1a

1b

Belladonna Lily
Amaryllis bella-donna L.

Amaryllidaceae

Amaryllis bella-donna is a native of South Africa, indigenous to the region between 30° and 35° latitude. It grows on the dry, grassy, coastal plains as well as on the steppes and plateaux of the interior. Breeding and selection have given rise to many ornamental forms with striking flowers that are popular for room decoration and in the greenhouse. The Belladonna Lily is often mistaken for plants of the genus *Hippeastrum* Herbert, which are native to Mexico and South America.

All parts of the plant, but principally the bulb, contain the poisonous alkaloid bellamarine, one of the many extremely poisonous alkaloids of the Amaryllidaceae family.

Toxic doses cause muscular paralysis, loss of co-ordination and paralysis of the respiratory centre. Death is caused by asphyxia. There are no cases of dangerous poisoning on record (either in humans or animals) outside South Africa. The Hottentots used the extract from the bulbs of this species combined with the extract from the bulbs of *Boophone toxicaria* Herbert as poison for arrows. In the southern United States, the native species *Zephyranthes atamasco* Herbert of the same family causes a disease in horses called 'staggers'.

In ophthalmology, alkaloids of the Amaryllidaceae family are used to treat glaucoma; they are also used in the treatment of muscular paralysis, formerly also post-poliomyelitis conditions.

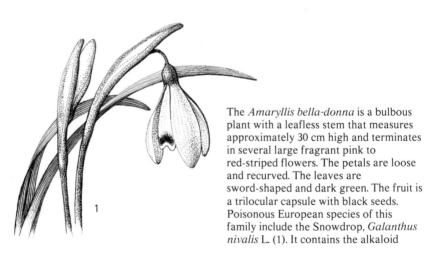

The *Amaryllis bella-donna* is a bulbous plant with a leafless stem that measures approximately 30 cm high and terminates in several large fragrant pink to red-striped flowers. The petals are loose and recurved. The leaves are sword-shaped and dark green. The fruit is a trilocular capsule with black seeds. Poisonous European species of this family include the Snowdrop, *Galanthus nivalis* L. (1). It contains the alkaloid

galanthamine, which is used in ophthalmology along with physostigmine (see *Physostigma venenosum*) for treating glaucoma. Galanthamine for medicinal purposes, however, is recovered from the bulbs of the species *G. woronowii* Los. Other poisons that primarily affect the heart are the alkaloids found in the bulbs of *Leucojum* L. and *Narcissus* L. There are cases on record of children being poisoned by eating these bulbs.

Fly Poison or Stagger Grass
Liliaceae
Amianthium muscaetoxicum Gray

Fly Poison, or Stagger Grass, as it is called in English literature, is found in North America in the states bordering the Atlantic, from New York to Florida, and westward to Kentucky and Arkansas. It grows in acidic soils in fields and open woodlands.

All parts of the plant contain poisonous alkaloids (0.1 per cent). Those that have been isolated to date include jervine, amianthine and two extremely toxic ester alkaloids. They are dangerous chiefly because they accumulate in the body organs. Cattle as well as sheep may be poisoned when grazing. Signs of poisoning are increased salivation, digestive disorders, vomiting, rapid breathing, lowering of the body temperature and giddiness. In the U.S.A., the poisonous juice from the plants is used to kill flies. Similar symptoms of poisoning are produced by the closely related species of the genus *Melantium* L., principally *M. virginicum* L., *M. latifolium* Desr. and *M. parviflorum* Wats., which grow in damp meadows in the Atlantic region of the U.S.A. These species cause poisoning chiefly in horses. Also related to the genera mentioned above is *Schoenocaulon* A. Gray. Its nine species, but mainly *Sabadilla* — *S. officinale* (Cham. et Schlechtend.) A. Gray, native to the mountain meadows of Guatemala and Venezuela, contain highly poisonous veratrine alkaloids in the seeds (see *Veratrum album*), e. g. cevadine, veratridine, and cevacine, in concentrations of 1—5 per cent. The seeds were formerly listed as officinal drugs in many pharmacopoeias under the name *Sabadilla.*

This bulbous perennial, up to 50 cm high, has a smooth, simple, leafless, flowering stem and sword-shaped basal leaves with parallel veins. The flowers are regular, trimerous and coloured white tinged with green. They are arranged in a short, simple, dense raceme. The ovary is superior and trilocular. The fruit is an inflated trilocular capsule with pointed tips (1) containing a large number of black seeds (2). Plants of the genus *Melanthium* do not grow from a bulb but from a rhizome. They are larger, reaching a height of more than 1.5 m, with white flowers arranged in loose panicles. The inflated trilocular capsules contain winged seeds. *Schoenocaulon officinale* has a like form and structure. The flowers, in dense racemes, are yellow.

1

2

Wood Anemone
Anemone nemorosa L.

Ranunculaceae

The genus *Anemone* L. comprises approximately 120 species distributed primarily in the northern hemisphere. The most common is *A. nemorosa,* occurring as several separate strains in Europe, Asia and North America. The Yellow Wood Anemone *(A. ranunculoides L.)* is another common species extending from Europe to Asia. Both are typical spring-flowering plants of broad-leaved woods, chiefly at lower altitudes, though they are found also in submontane as well as mountain districts. Many species of anemone are grown for decoration in the garden — chiefly the double and coloured forms.

Anemones contain the poisonous glycoside ranunculin, which by the action of the enzyme ranunculase gives rise to protoanaemonine. This is a very unstable substance which, when dried, breaks down into simple, non-poisonous compounds. For this reason, cases of poisoning are rare.

Externally, protoanaemonine is a skin irritant, causing painful blisters and, later, persistent ulcers. Internally, it causes acute inflammation of the digestive tract and kidneys and, in cases of severe poisoning, cramps, unconsciousness, and death through respiratory failure. In humans the primitive remedy for rheumatic pains of applying the fresh, crushed top parts or an alcohol extract to the painful spots causes severe damage to the skin. In animals, cases of poisoning are rare, although fatalities through respiratory failure have been recorded. Nowadays, the fresh top parts of anemone are used in folk medicine only occasionally as a revulsant in the treatment of rheumatism. The internal use of anemone extracts is not advisable because an extract from 30 plants will be fatal. The top parts of anemones are used to this day in homeopathic drugs.

1

Wood Anemones are low perennial herbs up to 20 cm high. They grow from a slender creeping rhizome at the beginning of the growing season (March — May). Often they are without even a single basal leaf, but that is offset by the palmately divided bracts beneath the flowers. The latter are relatively large (2—4 cm in diameter) and white with a violet flush outside. There are a great

34

many stamens with bright yellow anthers.
The fruit is a beaked achene. The Yellow
Wood Anemone *(A. ranunculoides)* (1) is
less common. The lovely white-flowering
Daffodil Anemone, *A. narcissiflora* L. (2),
is a protected species. All anemones,
including the cultivated forms, grown in
the garden, are poisonous. In Kamchatka,
the extract from anemones is purportedly
used to make poison for tipping arrows.

35

Upas Tree
Antiaris toxicaria (Pers.) Lesch.

Moraceae

The genus *Antiaris* Lesch. includes four species distributed in tropical Africa, tropical Asia, Indomalaysia and Oceania. Best known is the Upas Tree which grows in the tropical southern parts of India, Sri Lanka, Burma, southern China and Indonesia. For ages past, it has been known to the inhabitants as an extremely poisonous plant. The milky sap contains the poisonous glycosides antiarin and antiosidin, which exert a rapid and aggressive action on the heart, even more aggressive than that of the digitalis glycosides (see *Digitalis purpurea*). The first signs of poisoning — vomiting and diarrhoea — are followed immediately by a weakening pulse and cardiac arrest. The action is the same in animals as in man. The prognosis is always grave, only rarely does poisoning not end in death. The milky sap was used as poison, *'ipo',* for tipping arrows not only for warfare but primarily for hunting. Dutch sailors returned home with incredible tales of the tree's toxicity. It was said that birds fell to the ground dead when they alighted on the branches and that nothing grew in the vicinity of the tree, not even grass. It is a fact that few plants in Malaysia are more poisonous than the Upas Tree. To this day native phytotherapy uses the latex as a drastic cathartic and, externally, to remove painful ulcers. Attempts at using the cardiac glycosides of this tree in European medicine did not meet with success because of their relatively great toxicity and low stability in medicinal preparations.

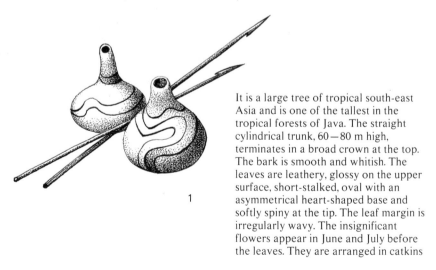

1

It is a large tree of tropical south-east Asia and is one of the tallest in the tropical forests of Java. The straight cylindrical trunk, 60—80 m high, terminates in a broad crown at the top. The bark is smooth and whitish. The leaves are leathery, glossy on the upper surface, short-stalked, oval with an asymmetrical heart-shaped base and softly spiny at the tip. The leaf margin is irregularly wavy. The insignificant flowers appear in June and July before the leaves. They are arranged in catkins

at the tips of the branches. The male
flowers have a large number of stamens
and longer stalks than the female flowers.
The fruit is an elongate berry covered
with fleshy scales and containing a hard
pit. The arrow poison *'ipo'* is prepared by
thickening the milky latex and then
combining it with aromatic admixtures
which increase its toxicity. It is stored in
calabash containers (1).

Indian Hemp
Apocynum androsaemifolium L.

Apocynaceae

The North American genus *Apocynum* L. includes seven species. The two illustrated here are *A. androsaemifolium* and *A. cannabinum* L., which are considered by some botanists to be merely two forms of the same species. They are found chiefly in the U.S.A., their range extending to southern Canada. They grow in fallow ground, neglected fields, gravelly pastureland and by streams from lowland to mountain districts. Because their stems have tough fibres which can be used for rope-making, they are both called Indian hemp. Attempts to use them more widely in the textile industry contributed to their present cosmopolitan distribution.

Both species, like most plants of the dogbane (Apocynaceae) family, contain poisonous cardiac glycosides, two of which are cymarin and apocannosid. Poisoning in humans, which happens only occasionally, causes heart failure. However, poisoning is quite frequent in horses and cattle grazing in open pastureland; approximately 15–30 gm of the fresh leaves may cause serious poisoning and even death. Symptoms are sudden lowering of body temperature, cold limbs, irregular pulse, dilated pupils, change in the colour of the skin round the nostrils, state of apathy and death.

The dried roots of both species used to be used, primarily in the U.S.A., for treating heart diseases. This practice was adopted in the mid-nineteenth century from Indian healers who used both species as diuretics and as emetics to treat dropsy. Later, the drug was replaced by pure, isolated cymarin but it is once again the subject of research in the quest for anti-cancerous substances.

2

Both species of *Apocynum* are robust perennials, up to 1.5 m high, with firm erect stems. They exude a poisonous milky juice when the stem is severed. The leaves are opposite, short-stalked and longish ovate. The flowers, arranged in terminal cymose inflorescences, are small and white or tinged with pink; the petals are joined for most of their length. The fruits are slender, sabre-like paired follicles, 5–20 cm long, that split along the ventral suture. The numerous seeds 1–2 cm long, have a pappus that falls readily (1). The two illustrated species are very similar. *A. cannabinum* (2) is larger and has narrower leaves and smaller flowers.

1

39

Columbine
Aquilegia vulgaris L.

Ranunculaceae

The genus *Aquilegia* L. has many species; more than 70 have been described. These plants are found mostly in the temperate regions of Asia and Europe; their centre of origin was probably eastern Asia. The species *A. vulgaris* is a typical member of the genus with a Eurasian distribution. It grows in patches in oak and beech woods and often up to sub-alpine areas. Its many, diverse, cultivated forms (differing in shape as well as colour) are grown for decoration in the garden.

The poisonous substances contained in the plant have not been fully identified as yet. They are glycosidic in character and their effect is that of cardiac poisons. Larger quantities (more than 20 gm of the fresh top parts or more than 5 gm of the crude, dried drug) cause cramps, breathing difficulty and heart weakness. These effects, however, are of relatively short duration. There is no record of animal poisoning; the plants are avoided by grazing cattle and drying causes decomposition of the poisonous substances thereby rendering them harmless in hay. In folk medicine Columbine was used externally to treat persistent eczemas and internally for gall bladder disorders. Nowadays it is no longer used in Europe except in homeopathy for treating neurosis, menopausal disorders and insomnia.

3

Columbine is a perennial herb with an erect branching stem up to 80 cm high. The leaves are pinnatipartite, lobed. The flowers are large, five petalled, with a blue, violet, pink or white calyx and long hooked spurs (1) filled with nectar. The fruits are follicles containing oval glossy black seeds up to 2.5 mm long. Some species are noteworthy for the shape of the leaves and the shape and colour of the flowers, e.g. the Japanese *A. flabellata* Sieb. et Zucc. (syn.: *A. akitensis* Huth), particularly the low forms var. *pumilla* (Huth) Kudo (2) and certain garden hybrids (3).

2

1

Birthwort
Aristolochia clematitis L.

Aristolochiaceae

The large genus *Aristolochia* L. (some 500 species have been described to date) has its origin in the tropical and sub-tropical regions of Central and South America. The best-known European species is *A. clematitis*. Its centre of distribution is the Mediterranean region and western Asia; in central Europe, it is probably not indigenous but naturalized. There it grows in waterside thickets, at the edges of groves and often in vineyards, in other words in warmer districts, and produces fruit only occasionally. The poisonous substances in the plant are aristolochic acids, chemically related to isoquinoline alkaloids. These cause serious disorders of the digestive tract accompanied by vomiting and diarrhoea. They cause inflammation of the kidneys and miscarriages in pregnant women. Death is caused by respiratory failure. Of the animals, horses are the most susceptible. They, too, suffer inflammation of the kidneys.

Folk medicine used the tincture from the top parts or rhizomes externally for rheumatic pains, to treat wounds and snake-bites as well as venereal diseases. Internally, it was recommended for gall bladder attacks and asthma. Later medicine used not only *A. clematitis* but also other species, for example *A. sempertaria* L., for numerous malaises, generally digestive disorders, as an antidote for snake-bite and for treating impotence. Studies are being made, at present, of the anti-cancerous effects of aristolochic acids, the effect of their external application on skin depigmentation (vitiligo), etc. Homeopathy uses aristolochia extracts externally for persistent eczemas, ulcers and for the healing of wounds.

Birthwort is a perennial herb with a simple, erect stem up to 1 m high. The leaves are alternate, heart-shaped, relatively large and long-stalked. The flowers are in loose clusters and are produced from May until June. The perianth segments are yellow and joined to form a slender tube inflated at the base and terminating in a large tongue-shaped lobe at the mouth (1). The inflated base contains the reproductive organs — the pistil and stamens. The ovary is inferior, composed of six carpels, six-locular, with numerous ovules. The fruit is a pear-shaped capsule with flat triangular seeds (2).

Some tropical species, e. g. *A. grandiflora* Sw. of Panama, are extremely poisonous. A few leaves will kill an animal and the plant is known to have been used with criminal intent.

1

Cuckoo-pint or Lords-and-ladies
Arum maculatum L.

Araceae

The genus *Arum* L. with its 12 species is distributed primarily in southern and central Europe. Its range extends north to Scandinavia, east to Iran and south to Algeria. *A. maculatum* is found throughout the whole range. It is a moisture-loving plant that is quite common in Europe's wet woods. It is also found in submontane and mountain areas, where it grows in beech and hornbeam woods. The poisonous substances of this plant are not precisely known.

It is presumed that besides volatile coniine-type alkaloids (see *Conium maculatum*) called aroines, the plant contains also poisonous saponins and perhaps even glycosidic substances that liberate hydrogen cyanide on cleavage. The poisonous substances are concentrated chiefly in the rhizomes and fruits. They are unstable and are destroyed by boiling, which is the reason why the starchy tuberous rhizomes were eaten, chiefly in the past, without any ill effects.

The plant juice produces blistering of the skin and mucous membrane, and the plant itself often produces a rash on contact, caused by the numerous oxalic acid microcrystals in the cells.

Internally, Cuckoo-pint causes diarrhoea, cardiac disorders and paralysis of the central nervous system. There have been cases of children who were fatally poisoned on eating the berries and also of cattle that fed on the plant while grazing.

In medicine, Cuckoo-pint was formerly used to treat instestinal worms but nowadays it is no longer used except in homeopathy.

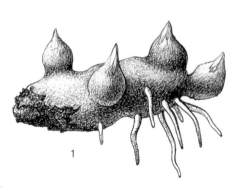

This perennial herb, approximately 20 cm high, has a tuberous rhizome (1) which bears long-stalked sagittate leaves. The flowering stem, appearing in April or May, is terminated by a violet to purplish spadix enclosed by a large, deeply cup-shaped spathe. The flowers in the lower part of the spadix are female, those above them are sterile and those still further up are male (2). The smell and colour of the spadix attracts insects which, coated with pollen from another Cuckoo-pint, enter the spathe and pollinate the female flowers, the stigmas of which secrete a sweet nectar. The insects are prevented from escaping by the curved bristles of the sterile flowers.

44

These wilt and the bristles droop, thereby
allowing the insect to climb out only after
the male flowers above have released
their pollen and the insect is coated with
it in readiness for pollinating other plants.
The fruit is a red globose berry about
1 cm across with a small number of seeds.

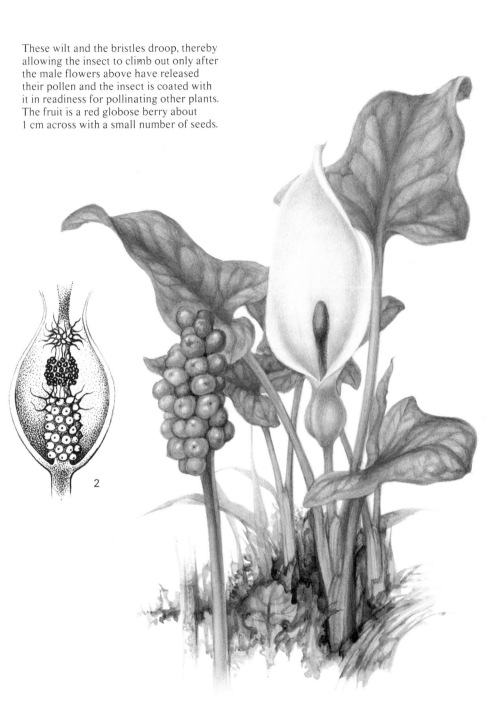

2

45

Asarabacca
Asarum europaeum L.

Aristolochiaceae

The genus *Asarum* L. numbers approximately 100 species, most of them found in southeast Asia. *A. europaeum* is a species commonly found in Europe, its range extending to western Asia and western Siberia as far as the Altai. It grows in open woodlands (mainly oak woods) and waterside thickets, primarily on limestone substrates, from lowlands to mountains. The poisonous essential oil (the rhizomes contain up to 2 per cent) contains numerous components, mostly asaron (30 per cent), methyleugenol (20 per cent) and bornyl-acetate (15 per cent).

Externally, it is a skin irritant and produces blisters. Internally, it causes vomiting, diarrhoea, inflammation of the kidneys, weakness and collapse. American literature cites cases of dermatitis caused by the leaves of the closely related North American species *A. canadense* L. There is no record of animals being poisoned by Asarabacca for they are put off by the peppery taste of the essential oil.

Asarabacca has been used for medicinal purposes for ages past. The rhizome was used to provoke vomiting, as a diuretic (it is still used for this purpose in homeopathy) and to treat asthma and inflammation of the upper respiratory passages. It is still used as a component of certain snuffs. Experiments with rats have shown that the essential oil may cause cancer of the liver and abortion. On the other hand, it also has a broad-range antibacterial action.

This small herb, only 10 cm high, has a creeping jointed rhizome from which rises a scaly and hairy stem. The leaves, which last the winter, are green and leathery, long-stalked, orbicular in outline with a deeply-cut heart-shaped base and entire margin. The flowers are solitary and short-stalked; the perianth is pitcher- or bell-shaped (1), greenish brown outside and dark purplish violet inside. There are 12 stamens arranged in two rings of six each. The ovary is six-locular, inferior and terminated by a six-lobed stigma. The fruit is a hairy ovoid capsule. The seeds have a spongy fleshy appendage (2) that is a favourite food of ants, which serve as agents of distribution.

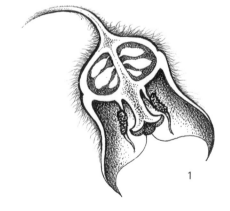

1

2

Deadly Nightshade or Belladonna
Atropa bella-donna L.

Solanaceae

Deadly Nightshade is a European plant, its range extending from western and central Europe east to the Crimea. It is cultivated and as such was introduced also into North America. It grows in woodland clearings and at the edges of woods, especially beech woods. The related species *A. acuminata* Royle ex Lindl. is a native of India. Both are important medicinal herbs.

They contain extremely poisonous tropane alkaloids, chiefly L-hyoscyamine, which partially changes by drying to DL hyoscyamine, or atropine. Other alkaloids, present in smaller amounts, include scopolamine, atropamine and belladonine. Belladonna poisoning is extremely dangerous, only 0.01 to 0.1 gm of tropane alkaloids being a fatal dose for humans. Symptoms of poisoning are dryness of the mouth, impaired speech, dilated pupils, blindness, followed by a state of excitement, then profound stupor accompanied by low blood pressure, difficulty in breathing, unconsciousness and death. The most frequent victims are children who eat the large juicy berries believing them to be edible woodland fruits. Some animals, e.g. birds as well as rabbits and cattle, are relatively immune, and poisoning is caused only by large doses. The Colorado Beetle even breeds and multiplies successfully on Belladonna.

Deadly Nightshade is a valuable drug in medicine; the pure isolated alkaloids are used as antispasmodics, antiasthmatics, and as agents affecting the functioning of the parasympathetic nerves.

1

Deadly Nightshade is a large perennial, up to 150 cm high, with a stout root and thick erect branched stem covered with large dark-green ovate leaves. The single five-petalled flowers (1) are borne from June until August. The corolla is brownish-violet, very occasionally yellow. The five stamens have large anthers. The ovary is superior, ovoid and bilocular (2). The fruit is a cherry-sized berry that is green at first, later blackish violet and juicy, with numerous small kidney-shaped seeds coloured pale brown. The berry remains subtended by the star-shaped calyx, which is flared when the fruit is ripe.

2

Red Bryony
Cucurbitaceae
Bryonia cretica ssp. *dioica* Jacq.

The genus *Bryonia* L. comprises approximately ten species distributed in the Mediterranean region and Turkey to Afghanistan. *B. cretica* ssp. *dioica,* together with the closely related species *B. alba* L., is found throughout this whole range. A climbing plant, it is frequent in hedges and waterside thickets, chiefly in relatively warm waste places. In central Europe, it has a widely scattered distribution.

It contains poisonous, glycosidically-bound cucurbitacines that chemically are triterpenoid-type bitter substances. The juice from the fresh plants or berries is a skin irritant and causes blisters on contact. Internally, excessive doses cause loose, bloody stools accompanied by abdominal pains, inflammation of the digestive tract and kidneys, as well as high fever. Forty to 50 berries are a lethal dose for adults, one-third that amount a lethal dose for children. Animals, particularly pigs, are affected by abdominal pains and diarrhoea after feeding on the roots.

Research has recently shown these substances to have a cytotoxic action and anti-cancerous effect by checking the growth of certain tumours. Cucurbitacines are therefore being carefully tested and ways of retaining the anti-cancerous effect while suppressing their extreme toxicity are being investigated.

The dried root is used in small doses as a drastic purgative in human and veterinary medicine. It is also used in homeopathy.

B. cretica ssp. *dioica* is a perennial vine of the gourd family with a large, turnip-like root. The rough, climbing stem is up to 4 m long and furnished with simple tendrils. The leaves are alternate, lobed and without stipules. The flowers are small and dioecious and are produced from June until September. The male flowers grow from the axils of the bottom leaves; they have a green, trifid corolla about 1 cm across and stamens arranged in three bundles with anthers on very short filaments (1). The female flowers (2) grow from the axils of the upper leaves; they are few in number compared with the male flowers and also less striking. The fruit is a small berry, less than 7 mm across, coloured bright red when ripe and containing two flattened ovoid seeds.

2

1

51

Bog Arum
Calla palustris L.

Araceae

The genus *Calla* L. has only one species, distributed in the northern hemisphere — in central and northern Europe, Siberia, Japan and the Atlantic coast of North America. It is a plant of bogs and wetlands found in lowland and foothill districts. It is relatively rare and, therefore, in many places is on the list of protected species.

It contains similar, if not the same poisonous substances as Cuckoo-pint, principally coniine-type alkaloids called aroines, and also saponins and glycosidically bound substances liberating traces of hydrogen cyanide on cleavage.

As Bog Arum is quite rare, cases of poisoning are not very frequent. However, instances of children having died after eating the red berries have been reported. Symptoms of poisoning are diarrhoea, inflammation of the mucous membranes, then a feeling of weakness and paralysis of the central nervous system. Grazing horses and cattle also have been known to die after feeding on the plant, although animals find its burning taste unpleasant and generally avoid it. Grave disorders of the digestive tract have been recorded in cattle that have fed on Bog Arum and the closely related Skunk Cabbage *(Symplocarpus foetidus* (L.) Nutt.*)* which is found in Siberia, Japan and Atlantic North America, and Jack-in-the-pulpit *(Arisaema triphyllum* (L.) Torr.*)* found in North America.

Bog Arum is a perennial herb up to 30 cm high with a green hollow cylindrical rhizome bearing long-stalked leaves with heart-shaped blade. The flowers appear in June and July and occasionally again in the autumn. The scapes, which are shorter

1

2

than the leaves, are terminated by a short spadix enclosed by a spathe. The spadix is cylindrical and greenish yellow, the flowers minute, without a perianth and densely clustered. The superior unilocular ovary contains 6—10 ovules attached at

the bottom of the ovary (1). The fruit is a sticky red berry (2) containing up to ten seeds. The seeds are elongate, approximately 5 mm long and longitudinally furrowed.

Marsh Marigold
Caltha palustris L.

Ranunculaceae

The genus *Caltha* L. comprises approximately 20 species that are found in the northern and southern hemispheres, except the tropical regions. *C. palustris* is found only in the northern hemisphere, in Europe, Asia and North America, often even in the arctic zone. It grows in damp places near springs, in wet meadows, ditches and wet woods.

It contains the poisonous but unstable protoanemonine arising by cleavage of the glycoside ranunculin. Protoanemonine and perhaps also saponins of which little is known as yet are what make Marsh Marigold poisonous. Its toxicity, however, is low compared to that of buttercups (see *Ranunculus acris*) because the concentration of poisonous compounds is low. That is why poisoning in both humans and animals is generally not grave. The poisonous substances are rendered harmless by drying (the plants are therefore harmless in hay).

There are cases on record of poisoning caused by eating fresh leaves of Marsh Marigold prepared as a salad and by consuming large amounts of pickled buds used as a substitute for capers. As for animals, cases of poisoning have been reported in sheep and goats. Symptoms are diarrhoea and cramps that disappear after a while. In the U.S.A., there have been cases of poisoning in cattle, sheep and horses that fed on the fresh plants.

Marsh Marigold was formerly widely used in folk medicine for rheumatism, as a diaphoretic and diuretic. Nowadays, it is used in homeopathy to treat itching skin rashes.

The Marsh Marigold is a 10—40 cm high perennial herb with a stout rhizome and procumbent ascending stem. The leaves that appear in spring are circular and heart-shaped with entire or scalloped margin and are glossy green above. The leaves that appear·after the flowers have faded are larger, with toothed or serrate margin. Marsh Marigold is a spring-flowering plant producing flowers from March to May, beginning in lowlands and ending in mountain districts. Occasionally it flowers a second time in the autumn. The flowers are large with bright, glossy yellow perianth segments (the perianth is undifferentiated). There are many stamens and the ovary is superior.

1 a

The tiny green flower buds of the prickly, trailing Mediterranean bush *Capparis spinosa* L. (1a, 1b) are poisonous and should not be mistaken for capers (see above). The fruits of Marsh Marigold are short-beaked follicles (2) with a large number of longish-ovoid seeds.

2

1b

Hemp
Cannabis sativa L.

Moraceae

Hemp is a cultivated plant with many varieties grown for its fibre and oil as well as narcotic substances. Hemp is probably native to the Far East and the Himalayan region but nowadays is grown nearly all over the world. The male plants are grown for their fibre and oil. In India, the Arab states and parts of Africa as well as in Mexico, Central America and South America, the female plants are cultivated; in the Americas they are the source of marihuana (the dried leaves and flowers) and in the Afro-Asian region the source of hashish (the resinous secretion from the leaves and female flowers).

Hemp, chiefly the female narcotic varieties contain, in addition to essential oils and traces of alkaloids, poisonous narcotic polyketids — cannabinoids — which produce a feeling of mild euphoria in users. The number of people using hashish today is estimated at more than 300 million. Animals are neither poisoned by nor do they become addicted to Hemp. The plant is little used in medicine; only occasionally is it prescribed in the form of a tincture or extract for its sedative and hypnotic effect.

Hemp is a dioecious annual herb with erect stem up to 2 m high. Some varieties are 1 to 1.5 m high, others, such as the cultivated variety 'Gigantea' grow to 4 m high. The stems of male flowers have few leaves, those of female flowers are more densely leaved. The leaves are palmately-compound, five- to nine-foliolate, the uppermost leaves being trifoliolate or undivided. The stem as well as the leaves are covered with glandular hairs. The flowering period is from June until August. The male flowers, in cymose inflorescences, have a five-segmented greenish perianth and five yellow stamens hanging out of the flower. The female flowers, in stalked clusters, have a short cup-shaped perianth and superior, unilocular ovary with two red stigmas. The fruit is an achene. The seeds are smooth and glossy greyish brown, 3—5 mm long and 2 mm wide; in the temperate regions of Europe they mature in September — October.

Rough Chervil
Chaerophyllum temulum L.

Umbelliferae

The genus *Chaerophyllum* L. includes some 35 species found chiefly in Europe and central and western Asia. Three species are native to south-eastern North America. *C. temulum* is a European species, even though it has been introduced into other continents. It grows in damp situations, such as waterside thickets, open woodlands, waste places and by walls and fences from lowland to hilly country.

It contains, primarily in the top parts and the fruits, the volatile alkaloid chaerophylline and other, probably glycosidically-bound poisonous substances that have been little investigated chemically or pharmaceutically as yet. Externally, the plant juice causes skin inflammations and persistent rashes. When ingested, it causes inflammation of the digestive tract, drowsiness, giddiness and cardiac weakness. Poisoning is rare in humans because the plant is not used in folk medicine and the fruits have no aromatic properties that could cause them to be mistaken for the fruits of other umbelliferous plants used as culinary herbs. Poisoning in animals has been recorded in cattle and pigs; symptoms are a wobbly gait, unsteady stance, apathy, and then severe, exhausting colic sometimes ending in the death of the animal. The symptoms of poisoning are similar to those caused by Common Carnel (see *Lolium temulentum*). The related species *C. bulbosum* L. and *C. hirsutum* L. are also poisonous.

The plant is not used for medicinal purposes except in homeopathy.

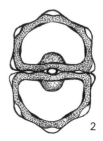

2

Rough Chervil is an annual or biennial herb with a spindle-shaped root and reddish stem, sometimes more than 1 m high, covered with long stiff hairs. The leaves are bipinnate with ovate leaflets. They may be spotted brownish red. Despite the marked difference between their leaves, Rough Chervil has been mistaken for parsley, with dire consequences. Rough Chervil flowers from May until July. The petals are white, occasionally reddish, and deeply notched. The fruit is a narrowly elliptical double achene, 5—7 mm long and 1.5 mm wide, coloured yellow-brown, sometimes flushed with violet, and striped with pale ribs and dark grooves (1). The fruit stalks are long and thick. In cross-section, the achenes are semi-circular and bluntly five-angled; the ducts containing the essential oil are located beneath the grooves (2).

1

59

Greater Celandine
Chelidonium majus L.

Papaveraceae

The genus *Chelidonium* L. has only one species, *C. majus*, distributed throughout all Europe from the Mediterranean region to Scandinavia and eastward to Asia. In North America, it is naturalized, not indigenous. It grows in humus-rich woods, wasteland, by walls and fences and by rural cottages.

All parts of the plant, including the roots, have lactiferous ducts containing a yellow latex with poisonous alkaloids which oozes out when the plant is bruised or broken. More than 20 alkaloids have been isolated to date. Those that have been most thoroughly investigated pharmaceutically are chelidonine, chelerythrine, sanguinarine, berberine, stylopine, coptisine and protopine. The concentration of alkaloids is greatest in the roots (up to 2 per cent), less so in the top parts (up to 0.6 per cent). Celandine is quite poisonous for man. Used as a home remedy in excessive doses, it has caused irritation of the mucous membrane, vomiting, loose bloody stools and blood in the urine. Forty grams of the extract from Celandine has been known to cause death due to heart failure. In animals fatal poisoning is rare because they avoid Celandine when grazing.

Medicine uses Celandine as a galenical (extract or tincture) or the pure isolated alkaloids as components of pharmaceutical preparations. Indications: disorders of the digestive tract, ulcers, gall bladder disorders. Of late, the cytostatic (anti-cancerous) effect of certain alkaloids in Celandine are being investigated but their high toxicity discourages their use for treatment.

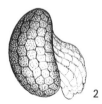

2

Greater Celandine is a perennial herb ranging in height from 30 to 100 cm depending on the site. It has a short branched reddish brown rhizome and erect branching slightly hairy stems. The leaves are pinnatipartite. The flowering period is from spring until autumn. The yellow flowers, with a great many stamens and superior unilocular ovary, are arranged in loose umbels. The fruit is a bivalved capsule opening along two sutures from the base to the tip (1).

The seeds (2), coloured black, are small, egg-shaped, up to 2 mm long, and furnished with a fleshy comb-like appendage that fits into a small hollow on the surface. This fleshy appendage is fed on by ants, which distribute the seeds, in crevices in dry walls for instance.

1

61

Cowbane
Cicuta virosa L.

Umbelliferae

The seven species that make up the genus *Cicuta* L. are distributed in the northern hemisphere. *C. virosa* is a native of Europe, its range extending through Siberia to Sakhalin and Japan. It grows in wet places: on muddy shores, in flooded meadows, ditches and in marshes. It is more common in the northern parts of Europe and Asia but relatively scarce in central Europe.

All parts of the plant contain the poisonous polyin cikutoxin, although the highest concentration is in the rhizome (up to 0.3 per cent). The essential oil (up to 1 per cent in the fruits) is also considered poisonous. Cowbane is one of the most toxic of all plants; about half of all the cases of poisoning in man are fatal. The action of the poisons is very rapid. The first signs are vomiting, giddiness and faintness, then convulsions resembling epileptic seizures which follow each other at increasingly shorter intervals until death occurs by suffocation within one hour after ingestion. Because the rhizomes have a sweet flavour, the victims are mostly children.

Animals likewise suffer convulsions and die after consuming only a small quantity of the green top parts or rhizomes. Horses and cattle are the main victims and, as drying does not affect the plant's toxicity, hay containing Cowbane is dangerous. In the U.S.A., cases of cattle poisoning by various species of cowbane, e. g. *C. maculata* L., have been recorded, particularly in spring when these plants start to produce leaves before other plants show signs of growth.

Because of its extreme toxicity, Cowbane is not used for medicinal purposes.

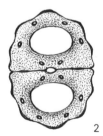

2

A perennial herb, generally more than 1 m high, Cowbane has a hollow glabrous stem and tuberous rhizome with transverse cavities. The rhizome and the lower part of the stem are generally submerged in water and the plant therefore also puts out roots from the nodes at the base of the stem. The leaves are two- to three-pinnatisect, the individual leaflets lanceolate with serrate margin. The leaf stalks, mainly those of the lower leaves, are hollow. The flowers

appear from July until September. The
petals are white with a heart-shaped tip.
The fruit is a broadly-ovoid double
achene (1) measuring 2 mm in width and
1.5 mm in length. The achenes do not
separate readily. In cross-section, they are
bluntly five-angled (2). They have five
blunt ribs filled with spongy tissue which
keeps them afloat, thereby aiding the
spread of Cowbane by water. The ducts
containing essential oil are beneath the
pale grooves between the ribs.

Colocynth
Citrullus colocynthis (L.) Schrad.

Cucurbitaceae

The genus *Citrullus* Schrad. consists of four species, some with a great many cultivated varieties such as watermelon (*C. vulgaris* Schrad.). The dry regions of tropical and southern Africa, the southern Mediterranean and India are the evolutionary centre of all four species. Colocynth *(C. colocynthis)* is found in tropical Africa, its range extending to southern Europe and the East Indies. It grows in sandy steppes and semi-deserts and is cultivated for medicinal purposes.

The fruits contain the physiologically-active glycosidically-bound bitter substances called cucurbitacines and a very bitter constituent, probably an alkaloid. The poisonous substances are not in the seeds but in the pulp. Their concentration in the other plant parts is much lower. The roots were found to contain poisonous saponins. The symptoms of poisoning are disorders of the digestive tract and inflammation of the kidneys and urinary passages, but nowadays these are caused only by excessive doses of medicines containing the fruits of Colocynth which are used in making a strong cathartic. Current research is investigating the anti-cancerous properties of the above mentioned cucurbitacines.

The sap from another species, *C. lanatus* (Thumb.) Matsum et Nakai var. *caffer* (Schrad.) Mansf. is used by African aborigines to make poison for their arrows. The Sutu of Africa use the pulp, which contains the poisonous alkaloid myriocarpine, as a strong cathartic.

In its native area of distribution Colocynth is a perennial vine; in more northerly regions such as Europe, it is an annual incapable of overwintering. In central Europe, it produces flowers from August until September and fruits in October, which is why it can be grown generally only in the greenhouse. The prostrate stem is 1−2 m long, roughly hairy and the same thickness (circa 5 mm) the entire length from root to tip. The leaves are five-lobed, roughly hairy, dark green on the upper surface and greyish green below. The tendrils are long and curled in a spiral. The male and female flowers, with yellow petals, grow from the axils of the leaves; the male flowers on the lower part and the female flowers on the upper part of the stem. The fruit is a large berry (1) the size of an orange.

1

coloured pale green at first changing to
yellow with yellow-green stripes and
containing a great many seeds. The fruit
pulp is dry, very bitter and has a foetid
smell. The fruit readily disintegrates when
it is ripe. The brown seeds are flat,
smooth, longish-ovoid and 6—7 mm long.

Meadow Saffron
Colchicum autumnale L.

Liliaceae

The species *Colchicum autumnale* is native to the Middle East and sub-tropical Africa. It grows mostly in damp meadows from lowland to mountain districts. All parts of the plant contain highly poisonous alkaloids, chiefly colchicine (localized in the seed coat in a concentration of 0.2−0.6 per cent), plus more than 20 other alkaloids such as demecolcine, which are used for medicinal purposes and are concentrated mainly in the corms.

Children and warm-blooded animals are the chief victims of dangerous and even fatal poisoning. The symptoms, which appear two to five hours after eating the plant, are a burning sensation in the mouth, vomiting, severe diarrhoea with bloody stools, blood in the urine, intense thirst, sudden lowering of body temperature, collapse and death, with the victim fully conscious, about 30 hours after ingestion. The amount of a fatal dose of colchicine for adults is 70 mg. Horses and cattle avoid Meadow Saffron even in forage. Only their young are occasionally affected when grazing. Goats and sheep are less susceptible, but their milk is poisonous after they have fed on Meadow Saffron.

Formerly, the crude drug (the corms or seeds) was used for medicinal purposes; nowadays, only the pure isolated alkaloids are used, namely colchicine, but more often the less toxic demecolcine. Indications: rheumatic pains, sciatica and certain cancerous diseases. Colchicine is also an important substance in experimental cytology. Its properties are used, for example, in breeding cultivated plants.

The genus *Colchicum* L., including *Bulbocodium* L. which is sometimes classed as a separate genus, numbers approximately 65 species native to Europe, the Mediterranean region, central Asia and India. Some species are grown as colourful and decorative rock garden plants.

2a

Meadow Saffron is a perennial herb with its corm wrapped in a brown membranous skin and buried deep in the ground. There are always remnants of the old corm beside the new one (1). Meadow Saffron flowers in the autumn, in September − October, producing one to three blooms that appear to grow directly from the ground, for more than half the long tube (up to 15 cm) is concealed underground. Only the upper part of the tube with violet funnel-shaped perianth

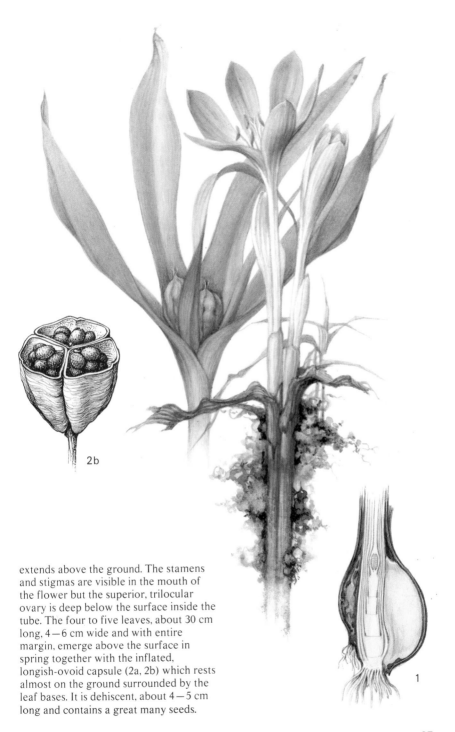

2b

1

extends above the ground. The stamens and stigmas are visible in the mouth of the flower but the superior, trilocular ovary is deep below the surface inside the tube. The four to five leaves, about 30 cm long, 4—6 cm wide and with entire margin, emerge above the surface in spring together with the inflated, longish-ovoid capsule (2a, 2b) which rests almost on the ground surrounded by the leaf bases. It is dehiscent, about 4—5 cm long and contains a great many seeds.

Hemlock
Conium maculatum L.

Umbelliferae

The genus *Conium* L. includes only two species. The one, *C. maculatum*, is native to Europe, Asia and northern Africa whence it was introduced elsewhere, including the Americas. The other, *C. chaerophylloides* Thunb., is a native of southern Africa. Both are weedy plants that grow on waste ground often near human habitation. All parts of the plant are poisonous; they contain piperidine alkaloids, principally the volatile, liquid alkaloid coniine, plus coniceine, conhydrine and others. The unripe fruits contain the greatest concentration of alkaloids (up to 2 per cent). Signs of poisoning are retching, vomiting, abdominal pains, inability to move the limbs, inability to swallow or speak, suffocation and death. The heart is not affected. Poisoning is generally due to mistaken identity: people eat the various parts of Hemlock believing them to be the leaves of parsley, the root of parsnip or the seeds of anise.

Of the animals, it is mainly pigs and cattle that are poisoned by feeding on Hemlock; geese and ducks also are susceptible. Sheep and goats, on the other hand, are more immune. Symptoms of poisoning in animals are paralysis of the limbs (paralysis of the skeletal muscles) and respiratory failure.

Galenical preparations from Hemlock were used formerly in minimal doses to relieve pain, to soothe and calm, and to relax muscular spasms, naturally with the great risk of poisoning if the doses were too large. Coniine is considered a carcinogenic substance, like nicotine (see *Nicotiana tabacum*). The use of Hemlock for criminal motives and for executions has been known since ancient times. Socrates was condemned to death in 399 B.C. by the drinking of a cup of poison containing Hemlock.

C. maculatum is an overwintering or biennial herb that smells of mice. It grows to a height of 2 m from a whitish spindle-shaped root. The stem is hollow, branched, furrowed, purple-spotted at the base (1) and seemingly covered with a bluish green bloom. The leaves are tripinnate. Hemlock bears small white flowers from June until September. The fruit is a broadly ovoid double achene up to 3.5 mm long (2), with five prominent wavy ribs. The essential oil is not in ducts but in special large cells inside the fruit (3).

2

3

The Sutu of South Africa and the
Mexicans poison fish by casting
Hemlock roots into the water as bait.
They also use another species, *Ligusticum
porteri* C. et R. of the Umbelliferae
family, for this purpose.

Forking Larkspur
Consolida regalis S. F. Gray

Ranunculaceae

The genus *Consolida* L., often classified into the large genus *Delphinium*, is found throughout the northern hemisphere. The species *C. regalis* is common in southern Europe and Turkey and has a limited distribution in the northern parts of Europe and western Siberia. It is a weed of fields, growing in hedgerows and fallow land, chiefly in warmer regions and in calcareous soil. Many cultivated varieties are grown as solitary specimens for decoration in the garden.

Forking Larkspur contains poisonous diterpenic alkaloids that occur also in other species of the Ranunculaceae family. Those that have been isolated to date include calcatripine, delsoline and delcosine.

There are no definite cases of human poisoning on record apart from allergic reactions. Cattle, however, are known to have been poisoned by this plant. Poisoning causes marked salivation, loss of co-ordination and, in serious cases, paralysis of the respiratory centre. North American literature contains many more references to the poisonous properties of Forking Larkspur. Some 18 species there are considered poisonous for cattle, horses and sheep. Their toxicity is ascribed to the presence of alkaloids with a curare-like effect (e.g. delphocurarine). Cases of poisoning are reported most frequently in the western United States.

C. regalis is no longer used for medicinal purposes; it is an obsolete drug. In folk medicine, the flowers and seeds are recommended as a diuretic and anthelmintic. Externally, the infusion from the top parts is used in the form of compresses to make wounds heal more rapidly. This, however, is a rather unsafe procedure not only because of the plant's toxicity but also because there is a danger that a secondary infection may be introduced into the wound.

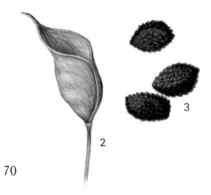

2

3

An annual herb, Forking Larkspur grows to approximately 30 cm high with a little branched quite slender stem. The leaves are divided into numerous thread-like segments. The relatively large flowers, which appear from June until September, are arranged in scanty terminal racemes. The calyx is blue-violet or, very occasionally, red or white. The upper sepal is paler and forms a long spur. The petals are joined at the base which forms

1

a spur concealed inside the spur of the calyx (1). The ovary is superior with a short style. The fruit is a light brown follicle (2) resembling a pod but splitting along a single suture and measuring up to 12 mm in length and 3 mm in width. The brown or black seeds are three-angled, small (1.9 by 1 by 0.8 mm), and are covered with rows of fine scales (3). A single plant may produce up to 400 seeds.

Lily-of-the-valley
Convallaria majalis L.

Liliaceae

Convallaria majalis is found in the temperate regions of the northern hemisphere; in the U.S.A., it occurs only randomly. Today, it is considered to be an extremely variable species, and some authorities even classify it as several different species. Lily-of-the-valley grows abundantly in oak and beech woods from lowland to mountain districts. It is also widely grown in gardens.

All parts of the plant contain numerous poisonous glycosides in concentrations of 0.2—0.6 per cent. Approximately 20 have been isolated to date; the most important are convallatoxol, convallosid (which gives rise to convallatoxin during the drying process) and locundjosid. Lily-of-the-valley also occurs as various chemical races: taxons found in western Europe are rich in convallatoxol, and taxons growing in eastern Europe are rich in convallosid. The glycosides of *Convallaria* are cardiac glycosides that have a pronounced effect on the heart muscle. Cases of poisoning are rare, generally occurring in children who have imprudently eaten the red berries. Signs of poisoning are irritation of the digestive tract, increased urination, heart weakness, and collapse. Animals are more likely to be poisoned by feeding on the leaves of the Lily-of-the-valley plant.

The dried leaves are used as drug and raw material for the isolation of glycosides for making cardiac medicines. These are popular medicines because the effect is fairly rapid and because they have a favourable diuretic action.

The essential oil from the flowers is widely used by the cosmetics industry to make perfumes and as an ingredient of other preparations.

Lily-of-the-valley is a perennial herb reaching a height of 10—20 cm. Every year in spring the creeping, jointed rhizome bears two or three smooth, stalked leaves, elliptic-lanceolate in outline with pointed tip and coloured a fresh green. The upright scape, appearing in late April and May, is terminated by a loose one-sided raceme of drooping milky-white flowers. The white perianth is bell-shaped with short spreading lobes. The six stamens with

deep yellow anthers are attached to the
base of the perianth. The ovary is
superior, trilocular and has a short style
with small insignificant stigma (1). The
fruit is a globose red berry with several
globose light brown seeds.

1

Common Crown Vetch
Coronilla varia L.

Leguminosae

The genus *Coronilla* L. numbers approximately 25 species distributed from the Mediterranean region through Europe to central Asia. *C. varia* is a native of Europe that was introduced (e.g. with the seeds of clover) into other continents, including North America. As a rule, however, it quickly becomes naturalized and seemingly indigenous. It grows in warmer regions on dry south-facing slopes, by the roadside and as a weed in the fields. It is also spread by cultivation, because for some time past it has been considered as possible drought-resistant forage. Its value as such is doubtful from the viewpoint of toxicology but it is a good plant for binding the soil and preventing the erosion of south-facing slopes and embankments.

It contains poisonous glycosides, mainly in the flowering top parts, that affect the heart muscle. The only glycoside that has been isolated to date is coronillin but there are probably several others. Excessive doses of the diuretic tea, used in folk medicine to treat disorders of the prostate gland causing obstruction of the flow of urine, caused poisoning, sometimes even resulting in death. The symptoms were nausea, diarrhoea, cramps and cardiac weakness. There are no reported instances of cattle being poisoned, but poultry, mainly chickens, have suffered severe diarrhoea and death after eating the seeds.

Common Crown Vetch is being tested as a possible substitute for Purple Foxglove (see *Digitalis purpurea*) in the treatment of heart disorders.

This is a perennial herb with a much branched firmly rooted rhizome. The ascending stem is more then 50 cm long and covered with alternate pinnate leaves. The flowers, borne from May till September, are pale pink, very occasionally white, and are arranged in a long-stalked umbel. As in all members of the pea family they are papilionate, the

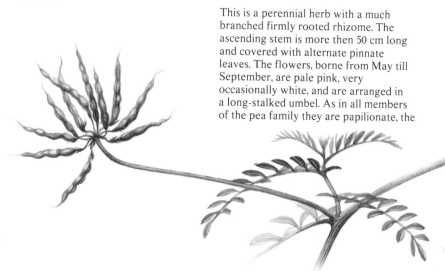

corolla having an erect upper petal (standard), two sickle-shaped lateral petals (wings) and two lower petals fused at their lower edges (keel). The fruit is a narrow legume, an upcurved dehiscent loment (1), 3—4 cm long, with several (about six) faintly constricted, one-seeded segments. The seeds are brown, occasionally dark red, cylindrical and measure 3 by 1.5 mm.

1

75

Bulbous Fumewort
Corydalis cava (L.) Schweigg. et Koerte

Papaveraceae

The members of the large genus *Corydalis* Vent. are distributed in the temperate regions of Europe, Asia and North America. *C. cava* is a native of Europe where, come spring, it forms lovely spreading carpets of violet and creamy-white flowers mainly in beech woods, oak hornbeam woods, groves and woodland clearings from lowland districts to the foothills. For this reason, it is widely cultivated in parks and gardens. The beauty of the flowers, however, is countered by the plant's toxicity. All parts of the plant, but chiefly the tubers, contain alkaloids of which more than 20 have been isolated to date. These are divided according to their structure into three groups: corydaline alkaloids, corycavine alkaloids, and bulbocapnine alkaloids. Bulbocapnine is the principal alkaloid of Bulbous Fumewort and also the one that has been investigated most thoroughly. It has a marked cataleptic action, causing the muscles to become rigid in the position in which a person or experimental animal was placed. The other alkaloids have a narcotic effect on the central nervous system. Cases of people being poisoned have not been reported to date, even though such poisoning is possible. There are cases on record of sheep having been poisoned; symptoms are staggering, faintness, cramps and death.

Bulbocapnine is used in medicine to suppress tremors in nervous diseases. However, it has a greater importance as a substance enabling the study of the action and responses of the central nervous system.

Every year from March to April (depending on the locality) the perennial herb, Bulbous Fumewort, produces a 15 to 30 cm high stem carrying two alternate leaves and ending in a dense upright raceme. The stem grows from a hollow brown tuber concealed deep in the ground. The leaves are twice trifoliolate.

The light or dark violet or creamy-white flowers have four petals; the two inner ones are fused and the two outer ones form an upper and lower lip, the upper lip being prolonged into a spur. The ovary is superior and unilocular. The fruit is a capsule that splits, after which the two valves fall (1). The seeds are black, glossy and globose with a fleshy appendage (2). Also native to Europe but not as common is the species *C. solida* (L.) Clairv., which differs from Bulbous Fumewort chiefly by having a solid underground tuber. As for the active constituents and their effects, there is no difference between the two species.

2

76

1

Croton
Croton tiglium L.

Euphorbiaceae

The genus *Croton* L. numbers approximately 700 species distributed throughout the tropical regions of the earth. Only a few species are found outside the tropics. *C. tiglium* is native to tropical Asia, where it is also cultivated. It was likewise cultivated in Africa. Nowadays, however, its cultivation is very limited because of the great toxicity of its oil. This is caused by phorbol esters. A single drop, that is 0.05 gm, is enough to cause diarrhoea; slightly higher doses may be fatal. Croton oil is obtained by pressing from the seeds, which yield 30 — 40 per cent. The seeds also contain the poisonous protein-phytotoxin crotin.

Although in the early twentieth century croton seeds were commonly found in the pharmacies of many countries, croton oil is no longer used in European medicine. However, people and animals still often get poisoned by croton oil or croton seeds in the tropics. The action of the poison is very rapid. Severe diarrhoea is followed by disruption of the metabolism and damage to the liver and kidneys. The resinous fractions in croton oil are also dangerous. Externally, they cause festering inflammations. Croton oil contains cocarcinogenic substances that can make the action of weak carcinogens many times stronger thereby causing cancer, an effect that would not be produced by the weak carcinogens themselves.

Croton grows as a shrub or small tree up to 6 m high with typically twisted slender branches and a bark coloured greyish white on the stem and brownish on the branches. The leaves are long-stalked and ovate with a nearly heart-shaped base; they turn red at the end of the growing season before they fall. The flowers are arranged in racemes at the tips of the branches, with female flowers at the bottom and male flowers at the top. The male flowers are greenish with protruding stamens (1). The female flowers have an ovary that rises prominently above the calyx and has three deeply-divided stigmas on a very short style (2). The fruit is an ovoid capsule the size of a hazelnut. The seeds are also ovoid, up to 1.5 cm long and 1 cm wide, dark brown with insignificant spots.

Croton oil was an important medicine in medieval times. Its use continued after this period and many pharmaceutical containers have survived to the present day. The receptacle (3) is of Antwerp majolica from the sixteenth century.

3

78

Broom
Cytisus scoparius (L.) Link
Leguminosae

Cytisus scoparius, often appearing in literature under the name of *Sarothamnus scoparius,* is a native of central Europe and the Balkan peninsula. Everywhere else, inside and outside Europe, it is a naturalized species. It grows on dry banks, in clearings and on pastureland, by waysides and at the edge of dry woodlands, chiefly oak woods. Its present distribution is the result of its being used formerly in folk medicine and also because it is widely grown as an ornamental shrub in parks and gardens.

All parts of the shrub contain alkaloids in a concentration of 0.3—1.6 per cent, primarily sparteine plus isosparteine, sarothamnine, lupanine and hydroxylupanine. Cases of poisoning are rare; they are generally caused by the excessive use of medicines containing these alkaloids or else by home treatment. Symptoms of poisoning are retching, vomiting, and diarrhoea, a cold sweat, feeling of weakness, difficulty in breathing, cramps, respiratory failure and death. As for animals, only sheep are known to have been victims; the poisoning, however, caused only temporary paralysis of the limbs.

In medieval medicine, the drug (the dried top parts of Broom) was used as a cathartic and diuretic.

Modern medicine uses mainly the pure alkaloid sparteine in obstetrics to speed up labour. It is also used with success in the treatment of arrhythmia to regulate the rhythm of the heart-beat.

2

Broom is a twiggy shrub or subshrub up to 2 m high with green, sparsely leaved branches. The leaves are small, mostly deciduous, the upper ones simple, the lower ones trifoliolate. The striking yellow flowers, arranged in what appears to be a racemose inflorescence, are produced in May and June. They are

large (up to 3 cm), short-stalked and
pea-like with recurved standard, blunt
wings and a slightly curved keel that soon
droops and falls away from the ovary and
stamens (1). The fruit is a long flat
legume with hairy sutures (2). As it splits
the two halves, or valves, curl up
and eject the black elongate seeds.

Mezereon
Thymelaeaceae
Daphne mezereum L.

The genus *Daphne* L. includes approximately 50 species native to Europe, Asia and north Africa. The species *D. mezereum* is found in Europe, its range extending beyond Siberia. It grows in open broad-leaved, mainly beech, woods as well as mixed woods from lowland to mountain districts.

All parts of the plant, but mainly the red fruits, contain the poisonous diterpene mezerein. The fruits are often the cause of poisoning in children; ten fruits are already a fatal dose. Symptoms of poisoning are a burning sensation in the mouth, salivation, abdominal pains, diarrhoea with bloody stools, painful urination, blood in the urine, cramps, difficulty in breathing, and collapse. Even less severe poisoning causes serious complications, starting with kidney damage. Externally, Mezereon or its juice causes inflammation of the skin, sometimes even blistering. Cases of poisoning in animals are rare for they find its bitter taste unpleasant and therefore avoid it. Nevertheless, several cases have been recorded of fatal poisoning in pigs after eating three (!) fruits and in horses after consuming 30 gm of the bark.

Folk medicine uses the alcohol extract from the bark as a liniment for rheumatic pains. Internally, it is used in a greatly diluted form in homeopathy.

D. mezereum, the same as other species of *Daphne,* e. g. *D. cneorum* L., is a popular early-flowering plant in the rock garden as well as in parks.

D. mezereum is a low shrub with firm
branches reaching a height of 150 cm.
The elongate oblanceolate leaves are
short-stalked and clustered at the tips of
the branches. The flowers appear in early
spring before the leaves, in clusters on the
sides of the twigs. They have a heady
fragrance. The coloured calyx resembles
a corolla, and its four segments are joined
at the base to form a tube (1). The
flowers are without a corolla. The ovary
is superior. The fruit is a deep red drupe
(2), containing globose oily seeds (37 per
cent oil), approximately 0.5 cm in
diameter and coloured brown.

The species *D. cneorum* is a small
shrub up to 40 cm high distinguished by
having leaves that remain on the plant
throughout the winter. Its fragrant red
flowers are arranged in an umbel (3).
Like all other species of *Daphne,* it, too, is
poisonous.

Datura arborea L.   Solanaceae

Tree-like members of the genus *Datura* L. are native to the tropical regions of Central and South America. They are distinguished by their strikingly large drooping flowers and for this reason are widely grown for decoration not only in tropical America but also in temperate regions as greenhouse specimens. Today, it is difficult to distinguish the species developed by multiple hybridization from the type species. The species *D. arborea* of the eastern coast of Central America was first described in 1714 by Louis Feuillée and his illustration was used by Linné for his description of the plant. According to present-day authorities, however, this species no longer exists as such; plants grown under this designation are mostly *D. candida* (Pers.) Saff. and *D. suaveolens* Humb. et Bonpl. ex Willd, native to Peru and Chile.

All tree-like daturas are poisonous. All parts of the plant, but primarily the leaves, fruits and seeds contain tropane alkaloids, mainly scopolamine. It is this that is also responsible for the narcotic properties used by the Indians in their ceremonial rites. The plants were also used for catching fish. Poisoning, when it occurs, is serious with similar symptoms to those caused by Deadly Nightshade (see *Atropa bella-donna*). Some tree-like daturas are cultivated commercially in Central America, South America and in the Caribbean region as raw material for the recovery of scopolamine. In folk medicine, besides being used in the form of cigarettes for their anti-asthmatic properties, they were also used in the form of plasters and compresses for rheumatic pains.

2

The perennial, tree-like plants of a woody nature reach a height of more than 3 m. The stems are rough, warty, and brownish at the base, whereas the tips and branches are green and herbaceous. The many, relatively large leaves are ovate-lanceolate in outline with an entire, usually wavy margin and dense network of prominent veins. The leaves of most species are hairy to a lesser or greater degree. The characteristic, drooping white flowers are more than 25 cm long in some species, with a flaring mouth. The

84

fruit is a soft spongy berry (1) containing flat kidney-shaped pale ochre seeds. The seeds have poor powers of germination and for that reason tree-like daturas are usually propagated by means of cuttings.

The map (2) shows the original area of distribution of *D. arborea* in South America. Species that are exceptionally lovely are *D. sanguinea* Ruiz et Pavon and *D. rosei* Saff. with flowers in various shades of red. Another beautiful example is the orange-flowering variety of *D. suaveolens.*

1

Thorn-apple, Jimson Weed
Datura stramonium L.

Solanaceae

The genus *Datura* L., comprises approximately 18 species distributed primarily in the tropical and temperate regions of the Americas. Most are herbaceous plants. *D. stramonium* is native to the southern regions of North America, chiefly Mexico, whence it was introduced into Europe by the Spaniards in the second half of the sixteenth century. Nowadays, it is found practically everywhere in the world where conditions are suitable. It grows on waste ground, usually near human habitation and in nitrogen-rich soils.

All parts of the plant contain very poisonous tropane alkaloids (0.2—0.6 per cent), mainly L-hyoscyamine, together with scopolamine. The effects of poisoning are severe, as in Deadly Nightshade (see *Atropa bella-donna*). Its victims are usually children who have eaten the berries. Otherwise poisoning is caused by excessive dosage. In animals, cases of poisoning have occurred in horses and cattle; pigs and poultry are fairly immune.

Thorn-apple is an important herb for medicinal purposes. The leaves are used by the pharmaceutical industry to make anti-asthmatic cigarettes and as a raw material for the isolation of alkaloids. More widely used for the latter purposes, however, are the species *D. metel* L., long cultivated in Asia, and *D. innoxia* Mill. of Central America, which is cultivated in Africa and India. In folk medicine, it is still used as a dangerous ingredient of 'love potions' and as a narcotic.

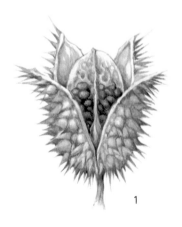

1

Thorn-apple is an annual, reaches a height of more than 1 m and flowers from summer until autumn. The stem is regularly branched and is thickly covered with dark green toothed ovate leaves. The bottom leaves are markedly larger than those at the tips of the branches. The flowers grow singly at the point of branching and are 10 cm long with a white gamopetalous corolla. The calyx is tubular and inflated at the base. The fruit is a spiny capsule that splits from the top, usually by four valves (1). It contains a great many seeds.

D. stramonium occurs as four varieties differing in the colour of the flowers (white and violet) and the number of spines on the capsules. The spineless

variety (2) was formerly described as
a separate species, *D. innermis* Juss. ex
Jacq. Several other annual species have
very distinctive capsules, e. g. *D. innoxia*
(3) and *D. ferox* L. (4).

3

2

4

Dutchman's Breeches
Dicentra cucullaria (L.) Bernh.

Papaveraceae

The genus *Dicentra* Bernh. with 17 species has two main centres of origin: North America and east Asia, or rather China. A single species is native to eastern Africa. *D. cucullaria* and the Canadian species *D. canadensis* (Goldie) Walp., are native to North America; these are both spring-flowering plants of open woodlands and pastures and occasionally they are found growing together.

They contain the poisonous alkaloid cucullarine, concentrated principally in the young shoots. *D. cucullaria* is more toxic. Besides cucullarine, it contains other alkaloid bases, of which little is known as yet, that further increase its toxicity. Cases of poisoning are regularly reported in the U.S.A. when cattle are put out to graze in spring, at which time the concentration of alkaloids in the top parts of the plant is at its highest. Serious cases have occurred most frequently in the mountain areas of Virginia. Symptoms of poisoning occur about two days after the first grazing: muscular tremor, frothing at the mouth, attacks of vomiting and heavy, difficult breathing. Although most of the herd survives, the affected animals require a lengthy convalescence. Similar poisonous properties are exhibited by the species *D. formosa* (Andr.) Walp., which occurs on the Pacific coast of North America from British Columbia to California.

Dicentras are not used for medicinal purposes, although formerly they were used by the North American Indians for treating toothache and intestinal worms.

2

1

Dicentras are perennial plants, 20—100 cm high. They have a tuberous rhizome and fragile branched stem with divided to greatly pinnate, greyish green leaves. *D. cucullaria* flowers from April until May. The flowers, short-stalked or nearly sessile, are arranged in a one-sided racemose inflorescence. The sepals are scale-like and soon fall; the two outer petals are inflated and semi-heart-shaped; the two inner petals are channelled. The fruit is a two-valved capsule with several seeds.

The species *D. spectabilis* (L.) Lem. of China (1) is well known in Europe, where it is grown as a garden perennial in several varieties. It has pink heart-shaped flowers (2). This species also contains poisonous alkaloids, e. g. sanguinarine, protopine and chelerythrine.

89

Burning Bush
Dictamnus albus L.
Rutaceae

Dictamnus albus is native to central and southern Europe, whence it spreads through Turkey and the Caucasus to the northern parts of China and the Amur River region. It is a thermophilous species found, in Europe, in stands of Pubescent Oak, forest-steppe, warm rocky scree and woodland margins, chiefly on limestone soils. It is also grown as a striking perennial in large rock gardens.

It contains the poisonous alkaloids dictamnine and skimmianine, plus saponins and an irritant volatile oil with a lemon scent. In people who are allergic to it, this volatile oil causes a skin inflammation and blisters, as does Rue (see *Ruta graveolens*), and the skin remains marked for a long time afterwards.

In folk medicine, the flowering top parts were formerly recommended as an aborticide. This sometimes caused fatal poisoning, the symptoms being severe inflammation of the digestive tract and kidneys, disrupted metabolism accompanied by gradual weakening and death due to cardiac arrest.

The alkaloid skimmianine is a cardiotoxic substance. It was first isolated from plants of the east Asian genus *Skimmia* Thunb. of the Rutaceae family and was named after this genus.

A robust perennial up to 1 m high, Burning Bush looks like a shrub with the top of the stems covered with glands. It has a stout deeply rooted whitish rhizome and firm erect twiggy stems. The stiff odd-pinnate leaves resemble those of ash *(Fraxinus* sp.) and were the reason why the plant was at one time named *D. fraxinella* Pers., a designation that is no longer valid. The fragrant flowers, arranged in terminal racemes, are produced in May and June. They are pentamerous and coloured pink with purplish veins or white; the stamens have long filaments and extend far beyond the petals (1). The fruit is a capsule composed of five follicles (2) that split on the inward-facing side. The inner layer of the pericarp separates from the harder outer layer, then suddenly bursts, twists and is ejected together with the glossy black seeds from the follicle.

2

Purple Foxglove
Digitalis purpurea L.

Scrophulariaceae

The more than 20 species of the genus *Digitalis* L. have their centre of origin in Europe and are indigenous chiefly in the southern parts of the continent. *D. purpurea* is exceptional in that its area of distribution is in western Europe from England and Ireland; the Harz and Sudeten mountains of central Europe mark its eastern limits. It is generally found in the foothills in woodland margins and clearings, always in non-calcareous soil. In garden cultivation, it is widely grown as a solitary specimen in natural rockeries and large gardens.

It contains extremely poisonous cardiac glycosides that affect the heart. The greatest concentrations are in the leaves (0.2—0.6 per cent). There are approximately 30 of these glycosides but the ones most thoroughly investigated and most widely used for medicinal purposes are digitoxin, digitoxigenin and gitaloxigenin.

Poisoning occurs mainly in patients treated over a long period with digitalis drugs, for in prolonged application the glycosides tend to accumulate in the body and build up to a dangerous level. Symptoms of poisoning are nausea, colour-tinted vision, irregular heart-beat, difficulty in breathing and, in serious cases, cardiac arrest.

Animals may be poisoned by feeding on foxglove when grazing or on hay containing foxglove. Cases of poisoning have been reported in horses, cattle, sheep and goats as well as poultry.

Foxgloves, today principally the Balkan species *D. lanata* Ehrh., are an irreplaceable source of cardiac medicines. Foxglove was used in folk medicine in Ireland whence it was first introduced to medical practice by the English physician W. Withering in 1775.

1

It is a biennial herb more than 1 m high forming a thick ground rosette of grey-felted ovate-lanceolate leaves in the first year. During the second year it produces one or several flowering stems bearing large flowers in one-sided racemes in June and July. The flowers are gametopetalous, tubular bell-shaped and generally coloured red with darker red, pale-edged spots on the inside.

Sometimes the terminal flower in the raceme is peloric (1). The fruit is a hairy ovoid capsule enclosed by the persistent calyx. It contains a great many small rust-coloured seeds.

2

The flowers of foxgloves are not
identical, e. g. those of *D. ferruginea* L.
differ in both shape and colour (2). All
foxgloves are poisonous.

Male Fern
Dryopteris filix-mas (L.) Schott

Aspidiaceae

The large genus *Dryopteris* Adans. has an almost universal distribution. The species *D. filix-mas* is found throughout the northern hemisphere except the arctic region. It grows in damp shady places, mountain beech woods and on rocky slopes. It is also grown in gardens for its ornamental leaves and attractive shape.

The poison found in this fern is called filicin, which is a mixture of substances used in therapeutic doses to expel tapeworms. Excessive doses, however, are dangerous causing retching, vomiting, yellow-tinted vision, paralysis of the central nervous system and temporary and even sometimes permanent blindness. Grave hearing disorders have also been reported, and fatal poisoning ends in tetanus-like, spasmodic contractions, respiratory failure and heart failure. Animals, chiefly cattle, exhibit the same symptoms.

The greatest concentration of poisonous substances is in the rhizome and lower part of the leaf stalk. The extract from the rhizome combined with a cathartic was formerly used to expel tapeworms, both in human and veterinary toxicology. The extract damages the epidermis of the tapeworm and paralyses the muscles, causing the tapeworm to release its hold on the wall of the intestine and the cathartic causes it to be ejected. Successful therapy, however, depends primarily on specific, individual dosage. Nowadays, other, mostly synthetic medicines are generally used for this purpose.

The Male Fern is a perennial reaching a height of more than 1 m in nourishing, humus-rich soil but only 30 cm in poor soil. It has a large rhizome covered with blackish brown scales. The fronds are pinnate. The stalks are densely covered with rust-coloured scales. The sori on the underside of the frond (1) are orbicular and covered by a kidney-shaped indusium as shown in the diagram of a frond in

2

cross-section (2). The stalked sporangium bursts when ripe (between July and September) and releases the spores. The spores germinate and become scaly, green prothallia with reproductive organs. The union of the gametes produced by the prothallium then gives rise to a rhizome bearing fronds with spores and the entire process is repeated.

South African tribal medicine uses species related to the genus *Dryopteris* as an anthelmintic. Members of the genus *Pteridium* Gled. ex Scop., e.g. Bracken (*P. aquilinum* (L.) Kuhn) are used for similar purposes in folk medicine.

1

Duboisia myoporoides R. Br.   Solanaceae

The few species that comprise the genus *Duboisia* R. Br. are native to Australia and New Caledonia. *D. myoporoides* is a shrub or small tree that grows in the Australian bush. It contains poisonous tropane alkaloids, primarily scopolamine, often in concentrations of as much as 4–5 per cent. It also contains other alkaloids such as hyoscyamine, piturine and duboisine. It is said to occur as geographic races with higher concentrations of hyoscyamine (in the vicinity of Sydney) or higher concentrations of scopolamine (Queensland).

The effects of tropane alkaloids have been described already (see *Atropa bella-donna*). The higher concentration of scopolamine in Duboisias produces specific narcotic effects; the victim of poisoning rapidly falls into a profound state of narcosis. The symptoms are the same in cattle that have accidentally grazed on *Duboisia*. Australian aborigines chew the leaves of the species *D. hopwodii* F. Muell. for their narcotic effect. In the advanced stage of addiction as well as at the start of using the drug, they are often fatally poisoned. Because of the high concentration of scopolamine, Duboisias, especially *D. myoporoides* and *D. leichardtii* F. Muell., are cultivated commercially for the pharmaceutical industry. So far, attempts at acclimatizing Duboisias in Europe have not been successful, nor have attempts to produce high concentrations of alkaloids in experimental cultivation.

3   *Duboisia myoporoides* is a perennial shrub or small tree, less than 5 m high, with thin branches. The leaves are sticky ovate-lanceolate with entire margin, 10–12 cm long and 4–5 cm wide. The flowers, arranged in terminal inflorescences are quite small and insignificant. The calyx is bell shaped with five lobes, the corolla tubular bell-shaped and white (1) with a margin consisting of two lips. The fruit is a berry (2) with many seeds.

The map shows the distribution of the species *D. myoporoides* (3). Most of the useful species of the Solanaceae family are native to South America (members of the genera *Solanum, Capsicum, Datura* and *Nicotiana*). Members of the genera *Atropa, Hyoscyamus* and *Scopolia* are

native to the Old World. As for Australia, the only members of the Nightshade family indigenous to that continent, besides the endemic species of the genus *Solanum* (*S. laciniatum* Ait. and *S. aviculare* G. Forst. — source of the steroid solasodine), are those of the genus *Duboisia.*

1

2

Wood Horsetail
Equisetum sylvaticum L.

Equisetaceae

The genus *Equisetum* L. comprises 33 species, ten of them native to Europe and Asia. *E. sylvaticum* is one that is quite common. It is distributed throughout the northern hemisphere where it often grows in a mass in damp woods, beside springs and in mountain meadows. It and the related species *E. palustre* L. and *E. fluviatile* L. emend. Ehrh. characteristically found in damp situations are definitely poisonous horsetails. Their toxicity is due to the presence of alkaloids, chiefly palustrine (equisetine), and partly also saponins. Recent research has proved the presence of the enzyme thiaminase that depletes the body of the important vitamin B_1.

There are no cases of human poisoning on record, at least no fatalities. Poisoning may occur when one of the above species is mistaken for Field Horsetail *(E. arvense* L.) which is commonly used for medicinal purposes.

Domestic animals, however, particularly horses, have been poisoned, the symptoms being restlessness, muscular tremor (mainly the facial muscles), an unsteady, weaving gait and finally profound exhaustion sometimes ending in death. Cattle suffer severe diarrhoea, weight loss and a reduction in milk yield. The milk is bitter. The poisonous properties of Wood Horsetail are not destroyed by drying or storing as silage.

In medicine, Field Horsetail (*E. arvense* L.) is used as an effective diuretic. This property is due to the presence of saponins and flavonoid glycosides. Field Horsetail is also used to treat tuberculosis because of the high concentration of silicic acid (10 per cent.). Despite its relative harmlessness, however, its use is not recommended without the supervision of a doctor.

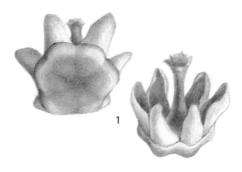

It is a perennial herb with jointed deeply-rooted rhizomes. In early spring, it produces fertile, virtually unbranched pinkish brown stems reaching a height of more than 50 cm. These terminate in cones composed of hexagonal disc-like sporophylls (1) on the underside of which are sporangia with spores. The spores germinate and develop into unisexual or bisexual green leaf-like and lobed gamete-bearing prothallia. From the union of the gametes produced by the prothallia develop stems terminating in spore-bearing cones and the entire

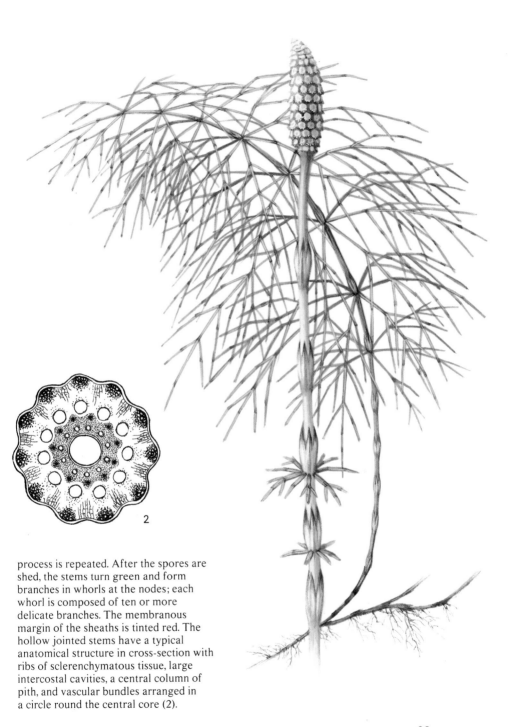

2

process is repeated. After the spores are
shed, the stems turn green and form
branches in whorls at the nodes; each
whorl is composed of ten or more
delicate branches. The membranous
margin of the sheaths is tinted red. The
hollow jointed stems have a typical
anatomical structure in cross-section with
ribs of sclerenchymatous tissue, large
intercostal cavities, a central column of
pith, and vascular bundles arranged in
a circle round the central core (2).

Coca
Erythroxylum coca Lam.

Erythroxylum coca formerly grew wild in the deep, warm, damp valleys of the Andes foothills in Peru and Bolivia, where it is now cultivated commercially, as it is in tropical regions in other parts of the world, e.g. in Africa (Cameroon) and Asia (Java).

The leaves contain approximately 1 per cent of poisonous alkaloids. The one most widely abused as a narcotic is cocaine, but among others are cuscohygrine, tropacocaine and truxilline.

Cocaine acts as a local anaesthetic in that it paralyzes sensory nerve endings thereby causing a loss of sensation. Used internally in a dose of approximately 0.05 gm, it acts as an irritant on the central nervous system, causing a state of euphoria, a feeling of well-being, talkativeness and sometimes hallucinations. Larger quantities cause cramps, paleness and feelings of anxiety, followed by giddiness, collapse and death due to respiratory failure and cardiac arrest. Even just 1 gm of cocaine is a fatal dose; a large quantity taken in solution causes almost instantaneous death.

Many of the Indians inhabiting the South American tropics chew the leaves of coca mixed with a small amount of lime or ash from Goosefoot (*Chenopodium quinoa* Willd.) to banish fatigue and hunger. This, however, often causes irreparable damage to the health. Cocaine addiction is a world-wide problem, and for that reason its distribution is prohibited except for pharmaceutical purposes.

In Europe nowadays, cocaine is used only to a limited degree for medicinal purposes in surgery, ophthalmology and dentistry. It was first used 100 years ago but has now been almost completely replaced by synthetic anaesthetics that are non-addictive.

Coca is a shrub or occasionally a small tree 1 – 2 m high with brown twiggy branches and firm wood. The leaves are alternate, short-stalked, longish-ovate and have an entire margin. The white, stalked five-petalled flowers (1a, 1b) are arranged in clusters of 2 – 5 flowers. The ovary is superior, ovoid and trilocular. The fruit is a smooth, one-seeded drupe about 1 cm long, coloured red when ripe.

Coca leaves are carried by the South American Indians in pouches called *'chuspas'* which are worn round the neck. They are made of leather or woven material and are usually richly decorated, as are the receptacles for lime or goosefoot ash that is mixed with coca leaves for chewing. The Incas stored coca leaves for religious purposes in decorated ceramic vessels (2).

1a

1b

2

101

Spindle Tree
Euonymus europaeus L.

Celastraceae

The genus *Euonymus* L. is a large one. Of the 220 species distributed in the temperate, sub-tropical and tropical regions, most are found in tropical south-east Asia. Several are indigenous to North America. *E. europaeus* is native to Europe, its range extending eastwards to the Caucasus, Crimea and western Siberia. It grows in humus-rich woods, on rocky slopes and in shoreline thickets, mainly in warm regions from the lowland to mountains.

The bark, leaves and fruits contain poisonous, markedly bitter peptidic and sesquiterpenic alkaloids that are chemically little known as yet and glycosidic compounds with a digitalis but relatively weak action. The seeds contain glycerine triacetate, a potential cathartic. Practically all species of *Euonymus* are poisonous.

Symptoms appear 12—16 hours after ingestion in the form of severe inflammation of the digestive tract accompanied by abdominal pains and diarrhoea. This is followed by disorders of the circulatory system, vomiting, a cold sweat and apathy. Cases of poisoning, sometimes fatal, have been reported in children who ate the berries. Horses, sheep and goats that fed on the leaves are reported to have shown symptoms of poisoning.

The Spindle Tree is virtually no longer used for medicinal purposes, although at one time the dried, powdered fruits were used externally to treat lice and scab. In the U.S.A., the bark from the roots of the native species *E. atropurpureus* Jacq. (Wahoo Bark) was used as a cathartic, diuretic and cardiac medicine. The oil from the seeds was used externally as a remedy for skin parasites and internally as a laxative.

2

The Spindle Tree is a shrub or small tree 2—3 m high with four-angled branches. The leaves are stalked, opposite, longish-lanceolate, about 10 by 3.5 cm, with prolonged tip and serrate margin. The flowering period is from May until July. The stalked four-petalled flowers, which have an unpleasant scent, are arranged in several axillary inflorescences. The corolla is greenish white (1). The fruit is a four-lobed, carmine-red capsule reminiscent of the biretta worn by Roman Catholic clergy. The seeds are enclosed by an orange aril. When the capsule is ripe and splits (2),

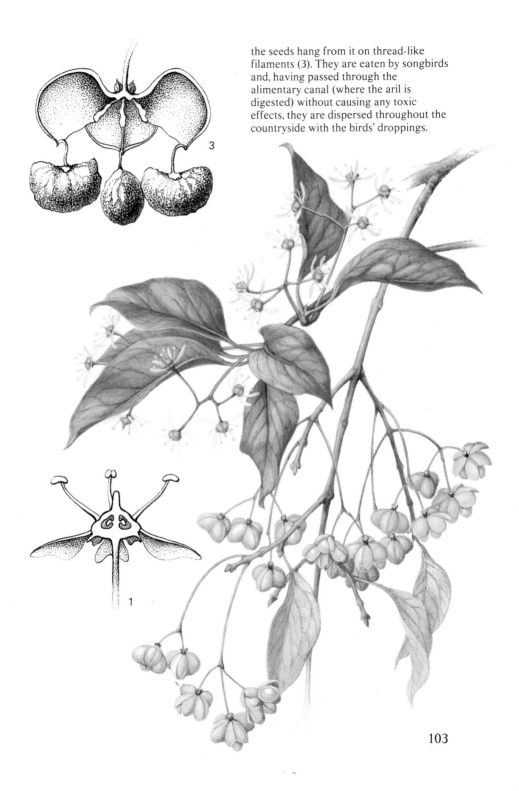

the seeds hang from it on thread-like filaments (3). They are eaten by songbirds and, having passed through the alimentary canal (where the aril is digested) without causing any toxic effects, they are dispersed throughout the countryside with the birds' droppings.

3

1

Cypress Spurge
Euphorbia cyparissias L.

Euphorbiaceae

Few genera have as many species as *Euphorbia* L. Some 2000 have been described to date, most of them native to the warm and sub-tropical regions of the world. Morphologically, they are distinguished by great variety and include succulent, herbaceous, as well as woody, plants (trees). Despite their great diversity they have one common characteristic: all exude a poisonous milky sap when bruised. The European species *E. cyparissias* is found almost everywhere in dry and sunny places: in hedgerows, pastureland, on the edges of fields and the like.

The poisonous milk contains the lactone euphorbon and the vegetable protein cytotoxin. It has a blistering effect on the skin and, if it enters the eye, it affects the cornea, causing ulcers, and may seriously damage the eyesight. When ingested, Cypress Spurge causes vomiting and diarrhoea accompanied by abdominal pains, disorders of the circulatory system, delirium and collapse. In cases of severe poisoning, the prognosis is bad. As for animals, even though they avoid the plant when grazing, cases of poisoning have been reported in horses, cattle and goats. The first symptom of poisoning in animals is extreme salivation, followed by colic, muscular tremor and a faltering, staggering gait.

In medicine, Cypress Spurge is used only in homeopathy. The essence from the fresh top parts is used greatly diluted to treat skin rashes and psoriasis. In folk medicine, it has been used for ages past to remove warts, corns and freckles. Its use as an anti-cancerous agent is questionable and dangerous.

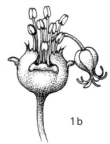

1 b

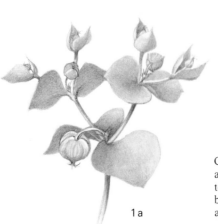

1 a

Cypress Spurge is a perennial herb with a woody branched rhizome and stems, up to 30 cm high, that ooze milk when bruised. Both sterile and flowering stems are erect, generally leafless at the base and covered with alternate almost linear leaves higher up. The flowers, which are produced between May and July, are greatly reduced and are arranged in a terminal inflorescence called a cyathium. The involucral bracts are yellow, becoming reddish in the fruit. The false 'flowers' are, in fact, the inflorescences (1a), which are composed of five stamens and a single pistil, five joined bracts and four marginal nectaries (1b). The fruit is a trilocular dehiscent, finely warty capsule containing three smooth ovoid yellow-brown seeds. One frequently comes across Cypress Spurges of atypical habit with leaves deformed by rust (2), for it is the specific host plant of the fungus that causes this disease.

2

Yellow Jasmine or Yellow Jessamine
Gelsemium sempervirens (L.) Ait.

Loganiaceae

Yellow Jasmine is native to the sub-tropical region of North and Central America, mainly the coast of Florida. It grows wild in natural shoreline thickets and is planted out in parks as a fragrant evergreen twining shrub for decoration.

The whole plant, but primarily the rhizome and the young flowering shoots, contain the extremely poisonous alkaloids gelsemine, gelsemicine, gelsedine and gelsevirine in concentrations of 0.1—0.5 per cent. They are typical convulsant poisons affecting the nerve centres (brain and spinal column), lungs and heart. Death is caused by paralysis of the respiratory organs and respiratory failure. Poisoning generally occurs due to excessive doses of medicines containing these alkaloids, but in the U.S.A. there have been cases of fatal poisoning in children who sucked the nectar from the fragrant blossoms. Veterinary toxicology has also recorded fatal poisoning in cattle, sheep, goats, horses and pigs which have fed on the leaves or rhizomes. The symptoms of poisoning are muscular weakness, jerky, spasmodic movements of the head and limbs, sudden lowering of the body temperature, slowed breathing, sweating and death due to respiratory failure.

In the pharmaceutical industry, dried extracts and tinctures from the rhizomes serve as a crude drug for the extraction of the alkaloids, which are used either in pure form or in mixtures to treat neuralgia, rheumatism, persistent coughs and asthma. The species *G. elegans* Benth., native to sub-tropical Asia (China), is known to have been used for deliberate poisoning.

A twining shrub, Yellow Jasmine grows to a height that varies more or less according to the height of the support. The rhizome is branched, 2—4 cm thick, with a great many suckers and roots. The twining stems are reddish brown and the persistent, opposite leaves are stiff, short-stalked, lanceolate with an entire margin, deep green, glossy on the upper surface and extremely decorative.

The yellow flowers appear in March and April and are solitary or in clusters of

three at the most. They are relatively large, 2—4 cm long and pentamerous (1). The corolla is funnel-shaped. The plant bears two types of flowers, either with stamens on long filaments and a short style or with stamens on short filaments and a long style. They have a pleasant fragrance. The ovary is superior. The fruit is a brown dehiscent capsule tapering to a point (2), with a large number of winged seeds.

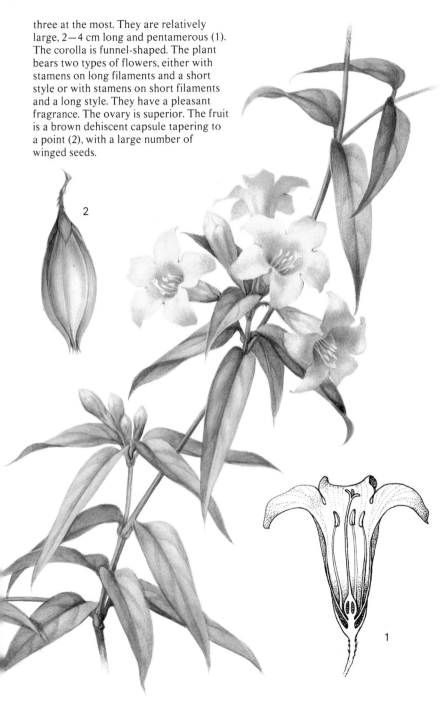

Hedge-hyssop
Gratiola officinalis L.

Scrophulariaceae

The genus *Gratiola* L. numbers some 20 species found in temperate regions or in the mountains of tropical regions. The species *G. officinalis* is distributed in central and southern Europe, its range extending to Asia up to western Siberia. It grows in damp to swampy locations, alongside water courses, often spreading into the water.

It contains poisonous bitter derivatives of tetracyclic terpenes, formerly thought to be glycosides with a digitalis effect (see *Digitalis purpurea*), plus cucurbitacines such as gratiosid. Toxic bitter glycosides that have been isolated are elaterinid and desacetylelaterinid with a strong cathartic action. These substances have an irritant effect on the digestive and excretory systems; in small doses they act as a laxative and diuretic but in larger doses they become extremely poisonous.

Recorded cases of poisoning are mainly of pregnant women, who have miscarried and even died as a result. The symptoms of poisoning are nausea, affected vision, vomiting, intestinal and kidney pains, loose, bloody stools, cramps, heart disorders, collapse and death due to respiratory failure. There are no cases on record of animals being fatally poisoned; mild cases have been reported due to the random occurrence of Hedge-hyssop in pastureland.

Because of its great toxicity and the variable effect of the crude drug (the dried, flowering top parts), Hedge-hyssop is used only occasionally for medicinal purposes. In medieval times, however, it was a prized medicinal herb for its strong cathartic, anthelmintic and diuretic action; it was also used for abortions,

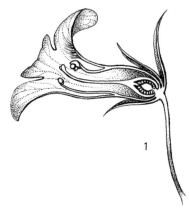

This is a perennial herb approximately 40 cm high with a creeping, jointed rhizome and hollow stems that are four-angled higher up, usually simple, and sparsely branched. The leaves are opposite, sessile, lanceolate, 3—5 cm long and dotted with glands. The flowers, appearing from June until August, are long-stalked and grow singly from the axils of the upper leaves. The broadly flaring funnel-shaped corolla with five lobes is approximately 1 cm long and coloured white with red veins; occasionally the lobes are flushed with red (1).

The capsule, containing several seeds,
is ovoid, four-lobed and dehiscent (2).

109

Christmas Rose
Helleborus niger L.

Ranunculaceae

The evolutionary centre of the genus *Helleborus* L. is the Mediterranean region, Turkey and the Caucasus. *H. niger* is a European species that grows wild in the foothills of the Apennines, Alps and southern Carpathians on limestone substrates. It is found in woodlands and on rocky scrubby slopes. Its mass of foliage and winter flowering soon made it a popular rock garden plant.

All species of hellebore are poisonous. They contain bufadienolid glycosides, mainly hellebrin and its aglycone hellebrigenin, that affect the heart. Another substance that has also been isolated is the steroid sapogenin.

As early as medieval times, the extract from the rhizomes was used as a deadly poison and as a questionable agent for treating the mentally ill. Children have been fatally poisoned by eating the seeds, and severe poisoning has been caused by drinking the milk of animals that have grazed on the plant. Poisoning causes a burning sensation in the mouth, extreme salivation, retching and vomiting, diarrhoea accompanied by abdominal pains, a roaring sound in the ears, visual disorders, irregular heart-beat and unconsciousness. Death is due to cardiac arrest or suffocation. Externally, the juice from the plant has an irritant action on the skin and causes blisters. The rhizome ground into a powder provokes sneezing.

Even though livestock generally avoids this plant when grazing because of its bitter flavour and unpleasant smell, instances of horses, cattle, sheep and goats being poisoned have been reported. Drying does not lessen its toxicity, and so hay containing hellebore is poisonous.

In medicine, pure hellebrin is used to a limited extent as a well-tolerated heart stimulant for tachycardia and heart failure.

The Christmas Rose is a perennial herb approximately 30 cm high with a thick unbranched blackish brown rhizome. The long-stalked leaves are pinnate and composed of 7—9 leaflets. The basal leaves remain throughout the winter. The flowering period is from December to March. The large hermaphroditic flowers, 6—8 cm in diameter, are arranged in scanty terminal inflorescences. The sepals are white to reddish. The petals are modified into yellow-green funnel-shaped nectaries. There are many bright yellow stamens and seven or more ovaries (1). The fruit is a follicle (2) with ovoid seeds (3). New leaves appear as the flowers fade, forming the rich clump of foliage that is characteristic of the plant in the summer and autumn months. The old leaves gradually dry up.

2

3

1

111

Goldenseal
Hydrastis canadensis L.

Ranunculaceae

Hydrastis canadensis grows in the shaded mountain forests of eastern Canada and the U.S.A. It was formerly cultivated in the north-western United States because it had almost disappeared from its natural habitats in the Atlantic region of North America due to over-collecting. Attempts at cultivating Goldenseal have been made also in Europe, where it was introduced as a medicinal plant in the late nineteenth century.

Goldenseal contains the poisonous alkaloids berberine (3 per cent), hydrastine (1.5−4 per cent), canadine (1 per cent) and berberastine. The toxicity of these substances may cause symptoms in people who have been given excessive doses of the drug or of medicines made from the drug. Poisoning in animals that have grazed on the plants is less common. Goldenseal causes severe ulcerous inflammations of the mucous lining of the digestive tract. Larger doses of hydrastine cause convulsions similar to those caused by strychnine (see *Strychnos nux-vomica*); it inhibits the action of the heart and also respiration. Berberine in small quantities has the same effect as a bitter principle; in larger doses, it has an irritant action on the central nervous system and later causes paralysis of the respiratory and motor centres.

The pharmaceutical industry uses the rhizome, the extract from the rhizome or the pure isolated alkaloids. These are used in medicine to check haemorrhaging in childbirth and painful, excessive menstruation. The effective substance in this case is the alkaloid hydrastine. In recent years, this drug, which had become nearly obsolete, has been the subject of renewed interest when it was discovered it had a partial anti-cancerous action. Goldenseal was formerly an important medicinal plant of the North American Indians who used it to treat chills, liver and stomach diseases and to check bleeding.

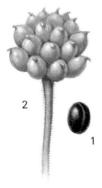

2

1

A slow-growing perennial herb, Goldenseal reaches a height of approximately 30 cm. It has knobbly rhizomes and several leaves, of which only one is usually fully developed; this is long-stalked and five-lobed with a serrate margin. The flowering period is in May − June. The flowers are solitary, terminal and hermaphrodite. The trimerous calyx

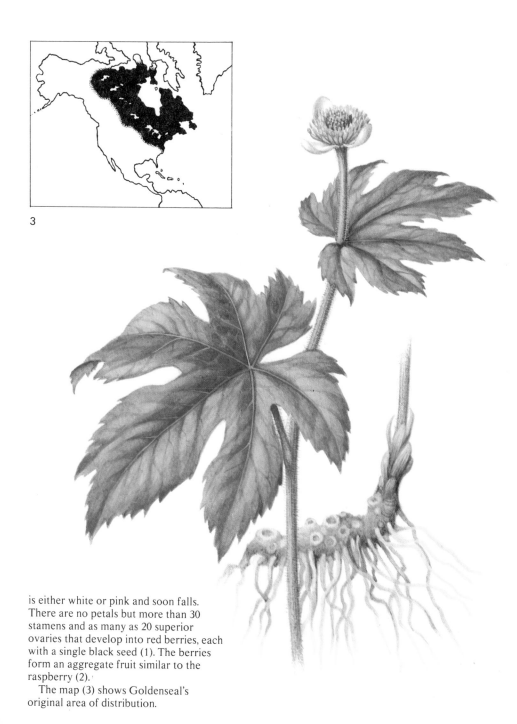

3

is either white or pink and soon falls.
There are no petals but more than 30
stamens and as many as 20 superior
ovaries that develop into red berries, each
with a single black seed (1). The berries
form an aggregate fruit similar to the
raspberry (2).

The map (3) shows Goldenseal's
original area of distribution.

Henbane
Hyoscyamus niger L.

Solanaceae

The original range of distribution of *Hyoscyamus niger* embraced Europe, western and central Asia, north Africa and India. Nowadays, it has an almost cosmopolitan distribution because it spread as a weed, was occasionally cultivated, and in many places where it was introduced even became naturalized. It is a plant of dry waste places — rubbish-tips, dumps — as well as the edges of fields chiefly in lowland districts.

All parts of the plant are extremely poisonous, especially the leaves and seeds. They contain tropane alkaloids (0.04—0.08 per cent), mainly L-hyoscyamine and scopolamine in a ratio of about 1:1. Even more poisonous is the north African species *H. muticus* L., found also in the Middle East. It contains 0.5—1.4 per cent alkaloids, chiefly L-hyoscyamine, and for this reason is cultivated commercially in Egypt.

Poisoning by these tropane alkaloids produces the same symptoms as does Deadly Nightshade (see *Atropa bella-donna*). However, if a person recovers from Henbane poisoning he often suffers irreparable mental damage caused by the high concentration of scopolamine. The consumption of 20—30 seeds is fatal for children; 100—150 seeds are fatal for adults. Henbane poisoning often causes double vision, painful spasms of the jaw and neck muscles, fits of rage and aggressiveness. There are no known cases of poisoning in animals. Modern medicinal therapy employs the leaves and seeds of Henbane only to a limited degree. The days of the plant's questionable fame as a narcotic and a component of love potions, poisons and ointments for Witches' Sabbaths during the Middle Ages are past and merely interesting historically.

3

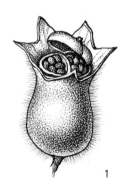

1

114

2

Henbane is generally a biennial, less frequently an annual herb, reaching a height of more than 50 cm. The root is spindle-shaped, the stem sticky with glandular hairs and a thick covering of alternate leaves. The leaves are ovate, with a sinuate coarsely toothed margin, and are sessile to semi-clasping. The flowering period is from June until September. The flowers, growing from the axils of the upper bracts, form monochasial cymes. The corolla lobes are dull yellow with violet veins or, very occasionally, whitish yellow without markings. The fruit, enclosed by the persistent pitcher-shaped calyx, is a bilocular capsule, approximately 1.5 cm long, that opens by a lid (1). It contains a large number of small brown kidney-shaped seeds (2). In medieval times, the leaves and seeds were stored in containers similar to those illustrated (3). The receptacles, painted red and decorated with escutcheons, are from Krems on the Danube and in all probability date from the early sixteenth century.

Japanese Star Anise
Illicium anisatum L.

Illiaceae

The more than 40 species of the genus *Illicium* L. have two centres of origin: Asia and America. In Asia, they are distributed from the Himalayas eastward to China, Korea, Japan and Indonesia. In America, they are found in the eastern parts of Mexico, south-eastern U.S.A. and the West Indies. The species *I. anisatum* is native to China but naturalized in Korea and Japan, where it is grown round temples and in graveyards. The bark and fruits are burned as incense at funeral rites.

The fruits are extremely poisonous. They contain the sesquiterpendilactone anisatine (according to some authorities, the alkaloid skimmianine) and cause severe inflammation of the digestive tract, kidneys and urinary passages; in larger doses they have a paralytic effect on the central nervous system. Poisoning generally occurs when the fruits of this poisonous species are mistaken for or added to the fruits of Star Anise (*I. verum* Hook. fil.).

The species *I. verum* is native to the mountains of southern China and parts of south-east Asia and is cultivated both there and in other tropical regions for its aromatic fruits which yield a culinary spice. Star Anise was first brought to Europe from the Philippines in 1588 by the English seaman Sir Thomas Cavendish, but it was not until the eighteenth century that this spice had spread across northern Europe into Germany. Modern medicinal therapy uses only the fruits of Star Anise *(Fructus anisi stellati)* as a digestive tonic, sedative and antispasmodic agent in the treatment of digestive disorders.

1

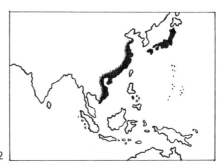

2

An evergreen tree of slender poplar-like habit with whitish bark, *Illicium anisatum* reaches a height of 10 m. The leaves are alternate, stalked, longish-ovate and leathery. There are numerous cells containing essential oil in the twigs and leaves, as well as the fruits. Unlike Star Anise, this species has a sharp, camphor-like scent. It flowers in April.

The flowers, growing singly from the axils of the leaves, have a perianth

composed of many segments. The outer ones are wider than the inner segments and are yellowish white or greenish. There are also a great many stamens. The ovaries, generally eight, have recurved beaks. The fruit is a follicle approximately 1 cm long and 0.25 cm wide, with smooth shining seeds. As they ripen, the follicles turn brown, become woody, split along the ventral sutures and spread out, the edges joined, to form a star (1).

The map (2) shows the centre of distribution of *Illicium anisatum*.

117

Rock Cedar or Savin
Juniperus sabina L.

Cupressaceae

The genus *Juniperus* L. numbers approximately 60 species often distributed over large parts of the northern hemisphere. *J. sabina* is a native conifer of most mountain districts in Europe and Asia, found chiefly on limestone substrates. It is also grown for ornament in parks and gardens, being a suitable shrub for dry places. Another species, *J. horizontalis* Moench., is a native of North America, found in the Great Lakes region and the Rocky Mountains. One characteristic the two have in common is that they are both poisonous. Besides other constituents, the essential oil of both contains the poisonous terpene alcohol sabinol and its ester sabinol acetate, plus sabinen and thujol. The young shoots of Rock Cedar contain up to 5 per cent of essential oil, of which the poisonous fractions comprise 50 per cent. Externally, the essential oil is a skin irritant, sometimes causing inflammation. The decoction or pure essential oil taken internally affects the mucous lining of the digestive tract causing vomiting and loose bloody stools; other effects are congestion of the lower pelvic region and, in pregnant women, miscarriage. This is followed by cramps, difficulty in breathing and paralysis of the central nervous system. Death occurs, with the victim in a state of profound coma, generally after several days or even later, due to incurable inflammation of the kidneys. About 1 gm of the drug or six drops of the essential oil form a toxic dose. Ruminants are susceptible to poisoning by Rock Cedar, whereas horses tolerate quite large quantities without harm. Due to its sharp unpleasant taste and relatively restricted occurrence, this plant is rarely eaten by animals. Rock Cedar is not used in modern medicinal therapy but it continues to be used in folk medicine as a dangerous abortive.

It is a coniferous shrub, occasionally of tree-like proportions, with spreading ascending branches covered with needles in younger specimens and with scale-like leaves in older individuals. The leaves are shed after about three years. The flowers are unisexual, occasionally monoecious but generally dioecious, and are borne on separate twigs thickly covered with scale-like leaves. The male flowers are longish-ovate, the female flowers have four yellowish spreading carpels which, after fertilization, develop into globose, cone-like berries measuring about 0.5 cm.

These are blue-black and contain three to
four seeds (1). They ripen in the autumn
of the first year or the following spring.

1

Common Laburnum or Golden Rain
Laburnum anagyroides Medic.

The genus *Laburnum* Medic. has only two species. *L. anagyroides*, native to the region extending from France through the Alps and Apennines to the Balkans, is today grown for decoration throughout the world in districts with similar climates. *L. alpinum* (Mill.) Bercht. et J.S. Presl has its centre of distribution in the southern Alps but is also found in the Slovakian section of the Carpathians. Both grow wild in broad-leaved woods in lime-rich soils, e.g. in karst areas.

Both species contain poisonous alkaloids: cytisine, methylcytisine, laburnine and laburnamine, which are found chiefly in the seeds (up to 3 per cent) and leaves (0.3 per cent). The effects of poisoning are vomiting, a cold sweat, cramps, dilated pupils, delirium and hallucinations. Cases are on record of children poisoned by eating the seeds from the pods. Ingestion of just two seeds suffices to cause symptoms of poisoning and death may occur within an hour after ingestion of a large number of seeds. Veterinary toxicology has recorded poisoning in horses resulting in muscular weakness, heart disorders and often death. Cases of poisoning in cattle, pigs and poultry have also been reported but are rarely fatal. Beasts of prey invariably vomit immediately after eating Laburnum.

Cytisine is used in modern medicinal therapy only to a limited degree for its irritant action on the respiratory centre, for migraine and for hysteria. According to the literature, however, results are not reliable.

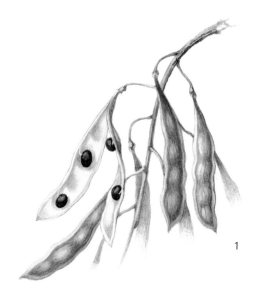

1

Laburnum forms a shrub or small tree generally up to 5 m tall with alternate, trifoliolate leaves. The leaflets are elliptical or ovate with a short point. The flowering period is April—May. The flowers are large, yellow and borne in striking, drooping, bractless racemes. They are characteristically papilionate. The corolla is pentamerous, with widely notched standard spotted brown on the underside, two spreading wings, and two bottom petals joined to form a keel inside which are ten stamens with filaments joined into one bundle. The superior ovary develops into a flat, finely hairy pod (8 by 1 cm) with flat dark brown seeds (1).

Greater Prickly Lettuce
Lactuca virosa L.

Compositae

Lactuca virosa is probably indigenous only to southern Europe (except the Balkan peninsula), north Africa and Turkey. In central Europe, it is apparently naturalized, having been formerly widely cultivated there as a medicinal plant.

The lactiferous ducts in the stem and leaves contain a poisonous milk, which pharmacies formerly stocked in thickened form under the name of *lactucarium*. It contains the specific bitter lactones, lactucine and lactucopicrine, in addition to other substances as yet undefined. These substances, which could be alkaloids, are also poisonous.

Poisoning is caused either by excessive dosage when used as a home remedy or, very occasionally, when the leaves have been added to salads. The symptoms are sweating, dilated pupils, a roaring sound in the ears, impaired vision, a feeling of pressure in the head, giddiness, drowsiness and disturbing dreams. There is no record of fatal poisoning. Animals are reported to have been poisoned by grazing on the plant. Symptoms in animals are sweating, faltering gait and, when greater quantities have been consumed, irregular heart-beat and a rapid drop in blood pressure.

Greater Prickly Lettuce was formerly cultivated for making lactucarium. The flowering plants were cut off from the top down as long as the milk oozed from the wounds. This was collected into small vessels and poured onto a wooden board to dry and thicken. Lactucarium was kneaded into balls weighing about 30 gm. It was used primarily as a narcotic, to induce sleep and to reduce the severity of coughing, and, mixed with the extract from hemlock and henbane, as an anaesthetic in surgery; later it was used as a substitute for opiates.

3

An annual or biennial herb approximately 1 m high, Greater Prickly Lettuce has a stem that is firm and erect and branched at the top. The leaves are alternate, ovate and spiny-fringed; the basal leaves are larger than the upper leaves. The flowers are in dense panicle-like inflorescences produced from June until September. The flowerheads are composed of about ten pale-yellow strap-shaped flowers. The

122

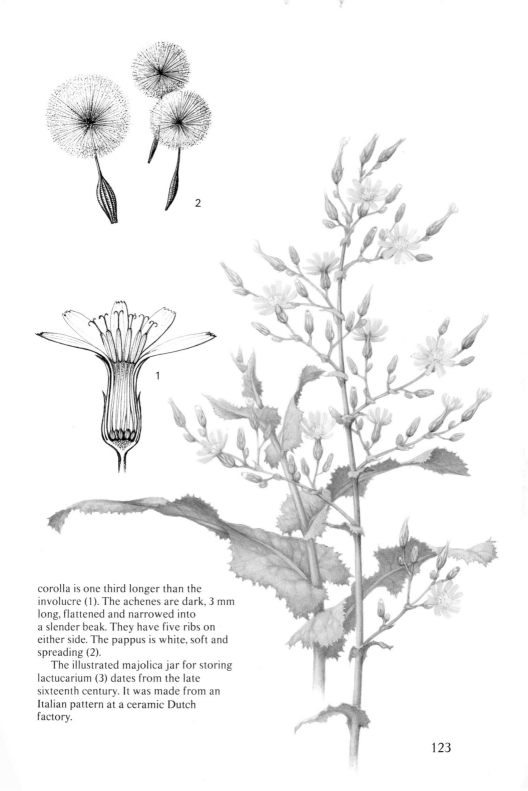

corolla is one third longer than the
involucre (1). The achenes are dark, 3 mm
long, flattened and narrowed into
a slender beak. They have five ribs on
either side. The pappus is white, soft and
spreading (2).

The illustrated majolica jar for storing
lactucarium (3) dates from the late
sixteenth century. It was made from an
Italian pattern at a ceramic Dutch
factory.

123

Wild Rosemary or Marsh Tea   Ericaceae
Ledum palustre L.

Ledum palustre grows in the coniferous woodland belt of the eastern parts of central and northern Europe, northern and central Asia, north Korea and Japan and in the cold parts of North America. It is found in scrub, heath moors and open pine woods. All parts of the plant contain an aromatic, poisonous essential oil, although the leaves and flowers have the greatest concentration (0.5—3 per cent). Its toxicity is due to the sesquiterpenic crystalline alcohol ledol and perhaps also palustrol. In recent years, doubts have been expressed as to the concentration of the glycosides arbutin and ericolin generally given in the literature but this is not a determining factor in the plant's toxicity. Ledol has an irritant action and, taken internally, causes a state of excitement and intoxication at first, later vomiting, abdominal pains and severe diarrhoea. It also causes congestion of the lower pelvic region, has an irritant effect on the kidneys and urinary passages, and may cause miscarriage in pregnant women. Further symptoms, in the case of larger quantities, are muscular pains, giddiness, cramps and collapse.

People are known to have been poisoned but, in animals, poisoning has been reported only in goats. Poisoning has ended in death for pregnant women who tried to abort the foetus by taking large doses of the extract from Wild Rosemary. Medicinal therapy used mainly galenical preparations from the crude drug (the dried flowering twigs or leaves): tinctures, infusions and, for external application, ointments. Ailments treated included rheumatic pains, whooping cough and inflammation of the upper respiratory passages. In folk medicine, Wild Rosemary is used externally to treat wounds (the essential oil has antiseptic properties), persistent eczemas and to destroy undesirable parasites.

Wild Rosemary is a small shrub reaching a height of about 1 m. Its habit of growth clearly indicates that it belongs to the heath family. The leaves are evergreen, leathery and linear to lanceolate in outline with a revolute margin. The flowers, produced in May and June, are fragrant, white or faintly pink, and are arranged in dense umbels. The calyx is five-lobed and sticky, the petals 0.5—0.8 cm long, the stamens (approximately ten) are longer than the corolla, and the ovary is superior (1). The fruit is a drooping 0.5 cm long capsule that opens by valves from the bottom up (2). The numerous minute spindle-shaped and winged seeds (3) are dispersed by the wind.

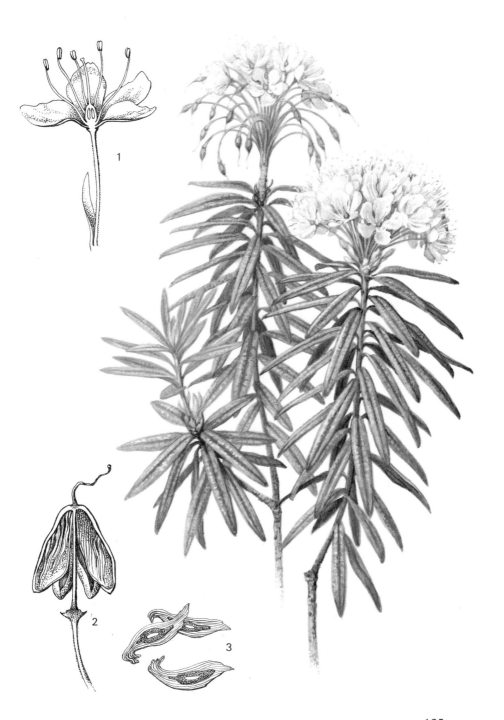

1

2

3

Indian-tobacco
Lobelia inflata L.

The genus *Lobelia* L. embraces approximately 380 species, most of them native to the tropical and sub-tropical regions of the southern hemisphere. *L. inflata* is native to the Atlantic region of North America, where it grows in meadows, pastureland and as a weed in fields.

All parts of the plant are poisonous. It contains some 20 piperidine and piperideine alkaloids in concentrations of 0.2—0.6 per cent. The principal alkaloid is lobeline; more important accompanying alkaloids are lobelanine, lobelanidine and their derivatives. Lobeline affects the respiratory centre; in therapeutic doses it has a stimulating effect, in toxic doses it has a paralytic effect and causes vomiting and collapse. Nevertheless no cases of fatal poisoning have been reported in humans. Cattle, however, have been fatally poisoned in the U.S.A. after grazing on *Lobelia* or being fed hay containing it. Symptoms of poisoning are severe retching, loss of motor control, dilated pupils, cramps and death. Related species have also been the cause of fatal poisoning, e.g. *L. siphilitica* L. (found in swampy meadows and pastureland in the eastern and northern United States) and *L. dortmanna* L. (growing in water and found also in Europe).

In modern medicine, the pure isolated lobeline is used for treating respiratory problems in newly-born infants, during anaesthesia and to relieve asthmatic symptoms. It is also a component of preparations used to help people stop smoking. The crude drug (the dried flowering top parts) was used by the North American Indians for the same medicinal purposes.

Lobelia is generally an annual herb up to 50 cm high with an erect angled grooved stem that is roughly hairy and reddish-violet at the base. The leaves are ovate to lanceolate and alternate, the lower leaves stalked, the upper leaves sessile. The flowering period is from June until August. The flowers are pale blue to whitish and arranged in spike-like racemes. The calyx is composed of five

3

sepals with long flaring awl-shaped points; the corolla is bilabiate, with bifid upper lip and trifid lower lip. The five stamens are joined to form a tube enclosing the style with its two-lobed stigma (1). The ovary is inferior. The fruit is a leathery inflated ovoid capsule with remnants of the calyx on top (2). The small seeds are spotted. The related robust perennial species *L. siphilitica* (3) was used to treat syphilis, hence the Latin name.

Common Darnel
Lolium temulentum L.

The evolutionary centre of the species that make up the genus *Lolium* L. is Europe, Asia and north Africa. Perennial Rye-Grass *(L. perenne L.)* is one of the species and is believed to be the oldest of all cultivated forage grasses. Some of the other species are considered poisonous by most toxicological literature. This applies to *L. temulentum*, which is a weed found in cereal crops the world over. *L. remotum* Schrank. is thought to be equally poisonous.

In 1892, Hofmeister isolated the liquid alkaloid temuline (its structure is still unknown) from the grains of Darnel. Later, it was believed that temuline was produced by a parasitic fungus that infested the plant. This theory, however, has been refuted by more recent works, for further protoalkaloid substances (loline, norloline, lolinine, perloline and others) have been isolated from other *Lolium* species. The concentration of alkaloids is said to become greater as the plant matures.

Symptoms of poisoning are stupor, lowering of the body temperature, partial paralysis and cramps. Fatal instances end in respiratory failure. Chiefly affected are domestic animals — horses, cattle, pigs and poultry. Formerly, before the grain was cleaned, humans, too, were frequently poisoned. Symptoms cited by victims also included vision, hearing and speech disorders, difficulty in swallowing and a feeling of fear.

Darnel is used for medicinal purposes only in homeopathy to treat vertigo, neuralgia and psychoses of unknown aetiology.

It is an annual, deep green to bluish green grass and reaches a height of 50—80 cm. The stems are stout, erect, and jointed, the leaves alternate and linear (less than 1 cm wide). Darnel flowers in June and July. The flat spike-like inflorescence, approximately 20 cm long, is composed of spikelets (1). These are large, 1.5—2 cm long and loose. The glumes are 1.5—3 cm long, thin and pointed. The lemmas are 0.5—0.8 cm long with straight or wavy awn (2). There are three stamens, and a smooth superior ovary with two feathery stigmas (3). The grain is elongate and remains enclosed by the lemmas when ripe.

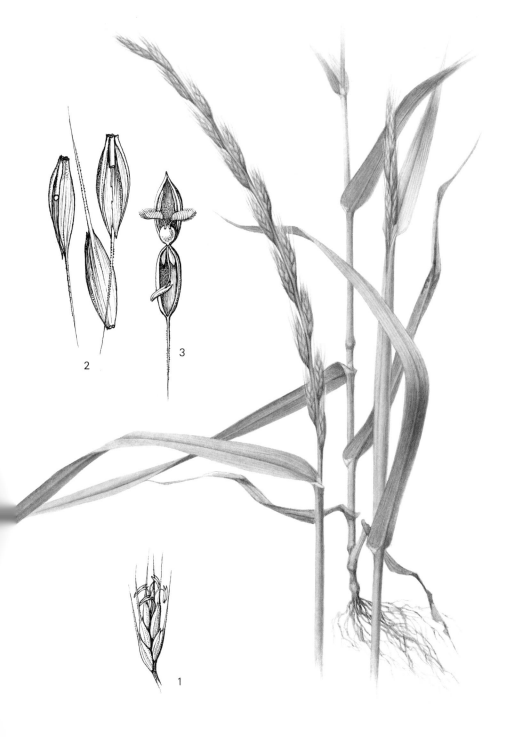

2

3

1

129

Black Honeysuckle
Lonicera nigra L.

Caprifoliaceae

The genus *Lonicera* L. embraces some 180 species distributed in the northern hemisphere and partly also in the South American Andes. The species *L. nigra* is native to Europe, its area of distribution extending to Siberia. It grows in both foothill and mountain areas in thickets, woods and woodland margins. Many cultivated forms are widely grown as hedges.

According to older literature, loniceras are poisonous due to the presence of the bitter substance xylostein. This assertion is generally repeated in later literature, but recent experiments have not proved it to be correct, for they have shown the presence of the phenolic substance syringin, the flavonoid glycoside lonicerin and saponins with a slight haemolytic action.

One thing is certain, however: several berries suffice to provoke retching, vomiting and abdominal pains in children. Fatal cases have been reported when children ate the berries of Fly Honeysuckle *(L. xylosteum L.),* which is common in Europe. Animals also exhibit symptoms of poisoning, chiefly retching, after eating the berries. Honeysuckle is employed for medicinal purposes only in homeopathy, which uses the essence from the fresh fruits to treat neuroses, spasmodic tremor of the facial muscles, senile shaking and the like.

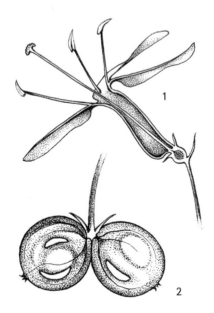

Black Honeysuckle is a shrub up to 2 m high with solid, erect branches and very hard wood. The leaves are opposite, short-stalked, longish-ovate and nearly glabrous. The flowers appear in April and May. The stalks of the two-flowered dichasiums are up to 4 cm long with small joined kidney-shaped bracts. The corolla is pink or tinted violet, 1 cm long, bilabiate and hairy inside. The ovaries are inferior and joined at the base (1). The fruit is a black pruinose berry about the size of a pea with elliptical seeds (2).

The species *L. caprifolium* L. (3) is a climbing shrub, twining in a clockwise direction, with tubular yellowish white often pinkish flowers up to 3 cm long that emit a strong fragrance, especially in the evening. It is widely grown for decoration in central Europe. This honeysuckle, which has red round berries, is also suspected of being poisonous.

3

Mescal or Peyotl   Cactaceae
Lophophora williamsii (Lem. ex Salm. Dyck) Coult.

Lophophora williamsii is found in southern Texas and middle Mexico, being most abundant in the region bordering the Río Grande. It is called pellote, peyote, peyotl or mescal by the local people. It grows in arid rocky deserts, rarely in large numbers. Only in certain districts is it more plentiful. In the Mexican state of Coahuila, for example, there is a village that is named San Jesús Peyote after this cactus; it is also one of the centres of traffic with the drug.

Mescal contains hallucinogenic alkaloids, principally mescaline (up to 6 per cent), plus anhalinine, anhalamine, lophophorine (the most poisonous of all) and others. Overdosage causes nausea, headache, giddiness and vomiting. Moderate doses, on the other hand, produce a state of excitement and hallucination accompanied by various feelings depending on the sub-conscious personality traits of the user.

Mescal is not used for medicinal purposes except in psychotherapy and very occasionally in cardiology. It is estimated that some quarter of a million people in Mexico and the U.S.A. use it for its hallucinogenic effects. The reason for this relatively small number is apparently the fact that the drug produces unpleasant effects immediately following ingestion, effects that precede the state of euphoria. Similar hallucinogenic effects are also produced by the Peruvian cactus *Trichocereus pachanoi* Britt. et Rose (San Pedro).

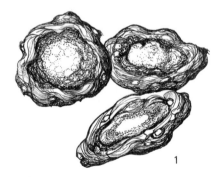

1

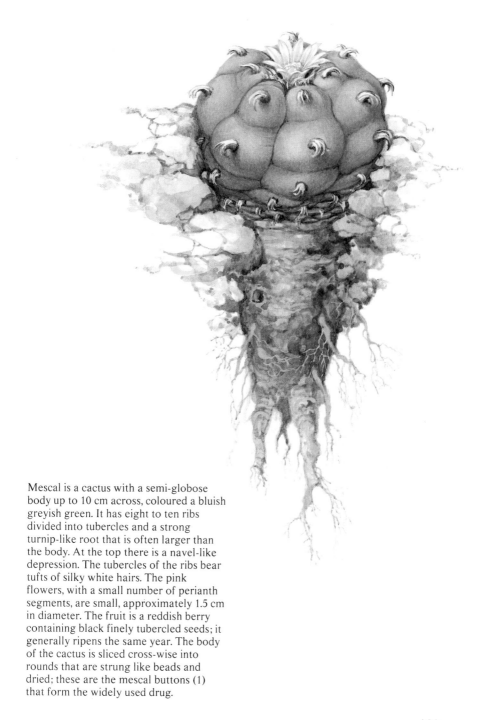

Mescal is a cactus with a semi-globose body up to 10 cm across, coloured a bluish greyish green. It has eight to ten ribs divided into tubercles and a strong turnip-like root that is often larger than the body. At the top there is a navel-like depression. The tubercles of the ribs bear tufts of silky white hairs. The pink flowers, with a small number of perianth segments, are small, approximately 1.5 cm in diameter. The fruit is a reddish berry containing black finely tubercled seeds; it generally ripens the same year. The body of the cactus is sliced cross-wise into rounds that are strung like beads and dried; these are the mescal buttons (1) that form the widely used drug.

Lupin
Lupinus polyphyllus Lindl.

Leguminosae

The genus *Lupinus* L. numbers some 200 species distributed chiefly on the Pacific coast of the Americas as well as in Europe, the Mediterranean region and tropical Africa. The species *L. polyphyllus* is native to North America where it grows wild in pastureland. It is much better known in Europe nowadays than is the species indigenous to the Mediterranean region. It is grown at the edges of woods and in woodland clearings as food for game, and some coloured cultivated varieties are grown for decoration in the garden.

It contains the poisonous quinilizidine alkaloids lupinine, sparteine, d-lupanine, hydroxyllupanine and others. Although wild animals remain unaffected, in livestock it causes a condition called lupinosis in veterinary toxicology. Symptoms of this poisoning, which is generally chronic but may also be acute, are restlessness, cramps, and hepatitis, ending in paralysis of the respiratory centre in fatal instances, usually in the case of horses and sheep; cattle and pigs are relatively immune. Chronic poisoning causes liver disorders and thereby poor digestion. It was discovered that the toxins of pathogenic moulds that often infest the plants, namely during the damp, growing season, are also dangerous. The poisonous toxins may also be present in the groats from the seeds of the lupin.

Occasional but severe poisoning has been reported in children after eating the seeds. The so-called 'sweet lupins' grown in Europe, ones that are without alkaloids as a result of breeding and selection, are less often the cause of digestive disorders and poisoning. North American literature, however, cites cases of poisoning caused by other species of lupin, ones that are not found in Europe.

Lupins are perennial herbs 1 – 1.5 m high, with palmately compound leaves (9- to 15-partite), the individual leaflets lanceolate, smooth on the upper surface and with silky hair below. The flowering period is from May until August. The blue to violet flowers with orbicular standards are arranged in long, upright racemes. The fruit is a many-seeded thickly-hairy pod.

The fruit of plants of the pea (Leguminosae) family may be a pod, loment or multi-seeded achene. Pods, in particular, are distinguished by great diversity of shape as shown in the

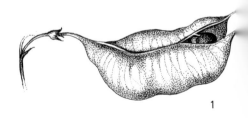

1

illustration of the fruits of several species: *Colutea arborescens* L. (1), *Ornithopus perpusillus* Brot. (2), *Melilotus officinalis* (L.) Lam. (3), *Medicago sativa* L. (4).

Rose Bay or Oleander
Nerium oleander L.

Apocynaceae

Nerium oleander is probably native to the Mediterranean region and the Middle East but has spread throughout the sub-tropical regions of the world where it is widely cultivated for decoration. In the Mediterranean region, it grows wild on the rocky slopes bordering the coast, except in maquis, chiefly in lime-rich soil.

It contains poisonous glycosides (principally in the leaves — 0.05 per cent) that affect the heart muscle. These include, for example, oleandrin, desacetyloleandrin and oleandrin monoglucoside. Medicinal therapy uses oleandrin (folinerin) in cardiology. Overdosage may lead to poisoning. Symptoms are vomiting, diarrhoea, irregular pulse, dilated pupils and, in severe cases, cramps and death due to cardiac arrest.

In places where Rose Bay grows wild poisoning may occur due to ignorance of its toxicity. Cases of dermatitis caused by contact with the leaves are common. Even meat roasted on twigs from the plant is poisonous. However, it has not been proved that honey produced by bees from Rose Bay nectar is poisonous, as some authorities state. Rose Bay is not used in folk medicine for its poisonous properties made people wary. There are cases on record of goats and sheep poisoned by grazing on the plant. Here, too, death is due to cardiac arrest.

Even though Rose Bay is not widely used for medicinal purposes, preparations containing pure isolated oleandrin are important cardiacs.

1

136

This is an erect, sometimes even large shrub or small tree up to 5 m high. The persistent leaves are simple, opposite, leathery, longish-lanceolate and pointed, with parallel veins. In places where it is indigenous, it flowers throughout the year, except during the rainy season.

The large cup-like flowers range in colour from red through various shades of pink to white or yellow (1). They are arranged in a cymose inflorescence. Inside the corolla are stipules modified into a scale-like corona. The superior ovary develops into a double follicle up to 15 cm long with felted seeds.

Tobacco
Nicotiana tabacum L.

Solanaceae

The genus *Nicotiana* L. numbers approximately 100 species of herbaceous as well as woody plants native to the sub-tropical regions of the Americas, Australia and certain islands of Oceania. The species *N. tabacum,* native to Virginia, is nowadays grown in many cultivated forms in sub-tropical and tropical regions throughout the world. Tobacco was introduced to Europe after the discovery of America. Until the early seventeenth century smoking (not only of tobacco) was not widespread in Europe. First to be smoked were pipes, followed by cigars in the early nineteenth century and in the mid-nineteenth century by cigarettes, introduced from Turkey.

The alkaloids found in tobacco — nicotine, nornicotine, anabasine, nicotirine and others — are very strong poisons. Pure nicotine is intensely poisonous on mere contact with the skin or mucous membrane. Taken internally in a dose of 50—100 mg it is fatal to man. When smoked, its toxicity is greatly diminished. All processes in the preparation of tobacco, beginning with fermentation, likewise decrease its toxicity, as do the auxiliary substances contained in the smoke. Nevertheless, the negative effect of tobacco, though milder, remains. This is testified to by the nicotine poisoning suffered by people starting to smoke and by that caused by excessive smoking. Symptoms are retching, vomiting, a cold sweat and cardiac weakness. Smoking causes chronic heart damage, inadequate supply of blood to the peripheral blood vessels of the limbs, ulcers, visual disorders, chronic inflammation of the respiratory passages and increased probability of lung cancer as well as cancer of the stomach.

3

A glandular pubescent cultivated annual plant, Tobacco has a firm erect stem ranging in height from 0.7 to 3 m, depending on the variety. The bottom leaves are large and elliptical, the upper leaves longish-lanceolate. It bears flowers in summer, depending on the place and variety. The flowers, arranged in panicle-like inflorescences, are large, with a pink corolla tube more than 5 cm long (1). The fruit is a longish-ovoid pointed capsule opening by four teeth (2). The many seeds are small, faintly kidney-shaped and spotted on the surface. The species *N. rustica* L. has

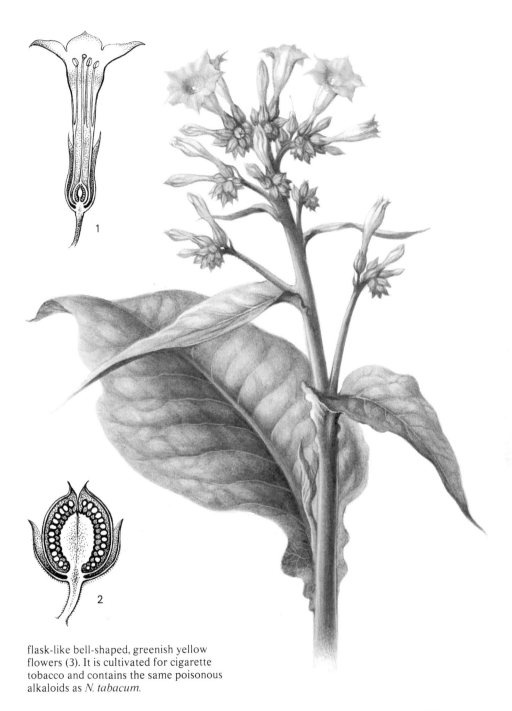

flask-like bell-shaped, greenish yellow
flowers (3). It is cultivated for cigarette
tobacco and contains the same poisonous
alkaloids as *N. tabacum.*

Yellow Water-lily
Nuphar lutea (L.) Sm.

Nymphaeaceae

Nuphar lutea is widespread in Eurasia and part of north Africa. It grows in still or slow-flowing, rather deep waterways. The rhizomes and leaves contain poisonous alkaloids. One, nupharine, more recently described as a combination of the two substances alpha- and beta-nupharidine, was isolated as early as the late nineteenth century. Not long ago, the Japanese isolated several pseudo-alkaloids (nitrogenic sesquiterpenes) from related Japanese species, e. g. nupharamine, nuthamine and nuphloine.

They have a sedative to narcotic action. Excessive doses caused paralysis of the brain centres in experimental animals. There is no record of poisoning by Yellow Water-lily either in humans or animals. In medicinal therapy, the alkaloids of this plant have been used only occasionally to treat extreme sexual excitation and emission (involuntary discharge of semen). Also used for the same purpose is the extract from the rhizome of the White Water-lily *(Nymphaea alba L.)*, likewise an aquatic plant with a virtually worldwide distribution. The rhizome contains effective alkaloids similar to those found in the Yellow Water-lily plus nymphaeine, which is extremely poisonous to fish. Not only alkaloids but also glycosides and tannins were isolated from the White Water-lily. The glycoside nymphaline recovered from the petals of the White Water-lily has also been found to have properties that stimulate the action of the heart.

2

The Yellow Water-lily is an aquatic perennial with a thick creeping rhizome anchored by its roots at depths of as much as 4 m. The leaf stalks are long; the blades, floating on the surface, are broadly ovate with a wide basal cleft and measure up to 30 cm across. The flowering period is from June until August. The flowers, which have an apple-like fragrance, consist of a globose calyx up to 6 cm in diameter composed of five yellow sepals and a corolla composed of many strap-shaped petals approximately one-third as long as the sepals. There are many stamens and a superior ovary (1). The aggregate fruit, composed of fleshy joined follicles, is 3—4 cm long, bottle-shaped and contains numerous seeds.

The White Water-lily is rooted at shallower depths (approximately 3 m) than the Yellow Water-lily. The calyx is green and soon falls, the petals numerous and coloured white to whitish pink. Some forms grown for decoration have pink (2) or azure blue flowers.

Common Peony
Paeonia officinalis L.

The genus *Paeonia* L. numbers more than 30 species found in the temperate regions of Europe and Asia; two species are native to the mountains of the Pacific coast of North America. *P. officinalis* is a native of Europe, of the region extending from the south of France to Albania. Peonies are all plants of scrubby mountain slopes and open woodlands. Certain species and their varieties are grown for decoration in the garden, e. g. *P. lactiflora* Pall. — so-called Chinese peonies native to the Far East, Korea and China — and the subshrub *P. suffruticosa* Andr., also of Chinese origin. All species are probably at least partly poisonous. They contain glycosides, most of which have not been investigated in great detail, namely paeonoside and paeonolid, plus apigenine, caempherol, and quercetine derivatives. Alkaloids described in the older literature, e. g. peregrine, have not been confirmed by recent investigation.

One thing is certain, however: ingestion of large quantities of the drug (the rhizome, seeds or flowers) causes nausea, vomiting, abdominal pains, congestion of the pelvic organs and faintness. Some of these effects have been newly confirmed by experiments with animals. Peony poisoning need not be fatal, but it causes chronic circulatory and digestive disorders, and miscarriages have been reported in pregnant women.

Peony is hardly ever used in modern medicinal therapy except in homeopathy and east Asian phytotherapy. Formerly preparations from Peony were prescribed for epilepsy, cramps, sciatica, and primarily as a component of anti-asthmatic and cough suppressant preparations (e. g. the well-known *Sirupus bromoformii*).

1

It is a perennial herb up to 60 cm high with a thick, spindle-shaped rhizome. The leaves are twice to thrice trifoliolate, dark green on the upper surface and pale green below. The stems are smooth and terminate in a single flower. The flowers, appearing in May and June, are large, 8—15 cm across, and coloured dark red or occasionally white. The calyx is persistent. There are generally eight petals, numerous stamens and two to three superior ovaries. The fruit is a follicle that bursts along the ventral suture and spreads open when ripe to expose the ovoid glossy blue-black seeds. The double forms of *P. officinalis* are grown for decoration in the garden. The species *P. mascula* (L.) Mill. (1) has follicles containing red partially deformed seeds that are sterile and bright violet-blue inflated glossy seeds that are viable.

Opium Poppy

Papaver somniferum L.

Papaveraceae

Papaver somniferum, probably native to Turkey, is a plant that has been cultivated for centuries. Its various varieties, grown for the oily seeds or for the production of opium, have been cultivated throughout Europe and Asia.

Opium Poppy contains a milky juice (latex) with numerous, extremely poisonous alkaloids, jointly called opium alkaloids. Opium is the dried latex obtained by making minute incisions into the unripe capsules, then scraped off and processed. Opium contains many alkaloids; a fatal dose for adults is 2—4 gm of crude opium which contains approximately 12 per cent of morphine. Morphine is the most toxic of all the Opium Poppy alkaloids: 0.25—0.5 gm is a fatal dose. In therapeutic doses, morphine has excellent pain-killing properties. In larger doses, however, it causes deep unconsciousness and death due to respiratory failure. Codeine is another opium alkaloid, one which has a far wider range of uses than morphine. It suppresses the cough reflex and potentiates the pain-killing properties of analgesics. Papaverine, another alkaloid of this group, has an anti-spasmodic action. All, however, are extremely poisonous in larger than therapeutic doses. Poisoning by opium alkaloids occurs when patients are given excessive doses of medicines containing these alkaloids and in persons addicted to morphine or its even more powerful derivative heroin. Used as a home remedy the decoction from the capsules (these contain opium alkaloids even after they are ripe and the seeds have been removed and are a valuable raw material for the recovery of these alkaloids) may cause severe poisoning which in children generally ends in death.

Opium Poppy is a cultivated annual plant richly oozing a milky juice. The stem as well as the alternate round-toothed leaves appear to be covered with a bluish green bloom. The flowers are produced between June and August, depending on the variety and the location. They are large and coloured white to violet with a dark blotch at the base of the petals. The calyx is green and soon falls. The stamens have dark anthers. The ovary is superior and globose with a multi-lobed stigma. The fruit is a capsule. The numerous seeds are small, pitted and coloured whitish, grey, pale blue or dark blue, depending on the variety.

Most crude opium is prepared for smoking by a complicated process. Smoking is one of the forms of opium addiction, one that originated in eastern Asia. Special, often richly decorated pipes (1a, 1b) are used for this purpose.

144

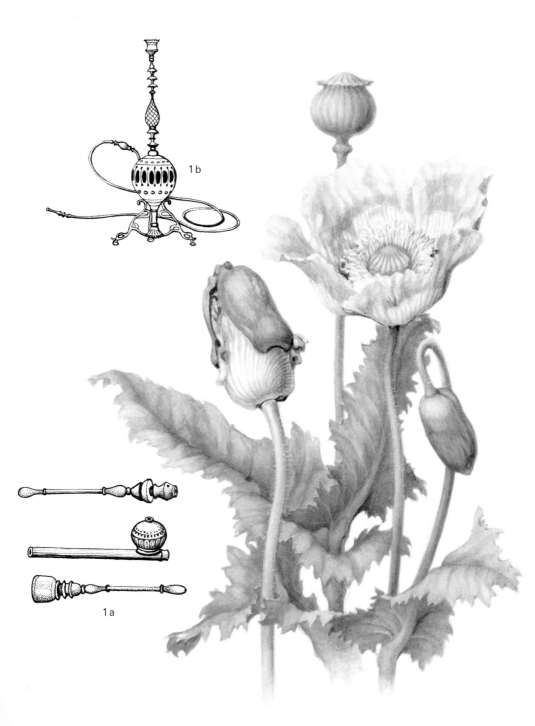

1 b

1 a

Herb Paris
Paris quadrifolia L.

The area of distribution of the species *Paris quadrifolia* covers Europe and part of Asia to the Altai and northern China. It is a characteristic plant of beech woods and broad-leaved woodlands up to the upper forest limit.

The toxicity of this plant is caused by the saponins paristyphnin and paridin, which are concentrated chiefly in the rhizomes and fruits. However, these poisonous saponins have not been subjected to recent chemical and pharmacological investigation. Because these highly poisonous saponins are absorbed very slowly, serious cases of poisoning are not common. They occur in children who have eaten the berries (two berries are enough to cause poisoning) mistaking them for large bilberries; but they have a repulsive taste and so are unlikely to be eaten after the first bite. Symptoms of poisoning are retching, vomiting, diarrhoea, constricted pupils, intense headache and a feeling of weakness. In some children, there is also retention of urine. In fatal cases, death was due to paralysis of the respiratory centre.

As for animals, it is almost only poultry that has been poisoned by this plant. The saponins in Herb Paris are also poisonous for fish.

Herb Paris is used only occasionally in homeopathy to treat vertigo, migraine and the after-effects of a stroke. Folk medicine formerly used the leaves in compresses to treat ulcers and stubborn wounds; this, however, was extremely dangerous in view of the possibility of infection.

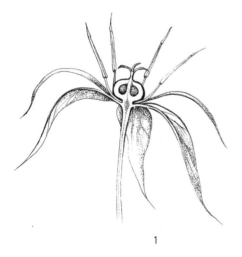

1

This perennial herb has a long, creeping, scaly rhizome. It reaches a height of approximately 30 cm. The erect stem bears a single whorl of four broadly elliptic leaves up to 10 cm long. Herb Paris flowers in April and May, sometimes even later. The solitary flower at the tip of the stem is tetramerous; the

2

outer segments are narrow, lanceolate
and pale green, the inner segments are
narrower, linear and yellow-green. The
eight stamens are arranged in two
concentric rings. The ovary is superior
and round (1). The fruit is a blue-black
berry (2) the size of a small cherry with
brown semi-globose wrinkled seeds.

147

Chinese-lantern Plant or Winter-cherry
Physalis alkekengi L.

Solanaceae

P. alkekengi is the best known European species of the large genus *Physalis*. It is native to the region extending from central Europe to the Urals, but elsewhere it is naturalized. It is often grown in gardens for decoration.

The rhizomes contain alkaloids: the poisonous hygrine, tigloyloxy-tropane and two other alkaloid bases not identified fully as yet. The leaves were found to contain steroid lactones, so-called withanolids (physalin A, B, and C), which are supposedly also poisonous. Most authorities are of the opinion that it is the rhizomes and leaves that are poisonous, not the fruits. Otto Gessner, the classic German authority on toxicology, includes the Chinese-lantern Plant in his list of poisonous plants. American literature considers it poisonous for animals, along with other related species such as *P. heterophylla* Nees. and *P. subglabrata* Mack. et Bush. In literature on poisonous South African plants, the species *P. minima* L. is listed as the cause of abortions in sheep. It is thus fully justified to suspect the Chinese-lantern Plant of being poisonous even though the fruits of certain American species, e.g. *P. ixocarpa* Brot. and *P. peruviana* L. are edible, and why not, when it is a well-known fact that the green top parts of the tomato (likewise of the Solanaceae family) are also poisonous due to the presence of tomatine and tomatidine, even though the fruit is an excellent vegetable.

The Chinese-lantern Plant was formerly highly prized by Arab physicians as a medicinal plant for treating kidney diseases (it purportedly disintegrated kidney stones) and diseases of the urinary passages. Today, it is used in homeopathy for the same purpose.

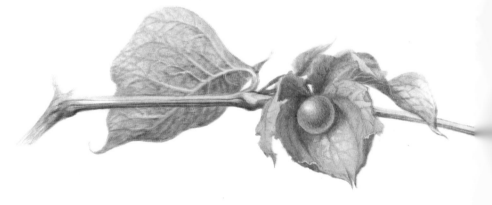

The Chinese-lantern Plant is a perennial
herb more than 50 cm high growing from
a creeping deep-rooted rhizome. The
stem is partly ascending and bluntly
four-angled with ovate leaves arranged
opposite each other practically in pairs.
The flowering period is from June until
August. The flowers grow singly from the
axils of the leaves. The calyx is
bell-shaped with five broad, three-sided
lobes at first. The dingy white corolla is
bell-shaped and five-lobed. There are five
stamens and the ovary is superior (1). The
fruit is a glossy red berry enclosed by the
calyx, which is inflated, bladder-like and
ribbed at this stage. The numerous small
seeds are approximately 2 mm long,
markedly flat, faintly kidney-shaped and
marked with a fine network pattern (2).

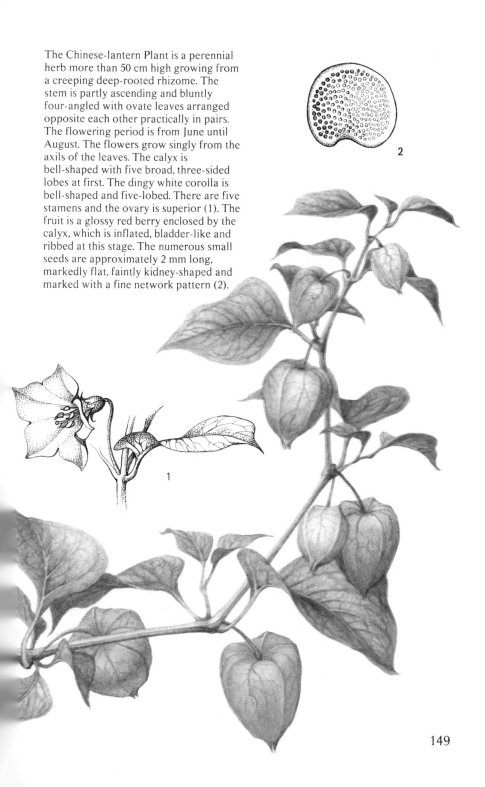

149

Calabar Bean Plant
Physostigma venenosum Balf.

The genus *Physostigma* Balf. includes two or three species native to tropical Africa. *Physostigma venenosum,* a tropical vine of the rain forest, is native to west Africa, chiefly the Calabar river region in Nigeria and Cameroon.

The seeds, called Calabar beans after their place of origin, contain 0.5 per cent of extremely poisonous alkaloids, principally physostigmine, also called eserine, derived from the word *éséré,* the local term for the seeds. The toxicity of the seeds has been known to the inhabitants of the area for many generations, and was used to determine whether the accused was guilty or innocent if a trial proved inconclusive. The accused had to drink a cup of water with crushed Calabar beans; if he died he was guilty, if not he was freed. In Zaire, 227 persons were executed by this method as recently as 1959. Calabar beans were also used to poison arrows for hunting as well as warfare.

Symptoms of poisoning are extreme salivation, constricted pupils, blurred vision, giddiness, severe vomiting, diarrhoea, a feeling of general weakness and death due to respiratory failure. The use of physostigmine in medicine dates from the mid-nineteenth century. It is used to contract the pupils and reduce pressure within the eyeball in the treatment of glaucoma, to decrease the heart-rate, to increase peristalsis in post-operative constipation and also to prevent muscular paralysis.

1

Calabar Bean Plant is a tropical vine up to 15 m long. It is woody at the base, herbaceous at the top and covered with trifoliolate leaves. The characteristic pea-like flowers, arranged in drooping axillary racemes, measure approximately 2 cm and are purplish green. Before they open, the furled flowers curve upward. The fruit is a long flattened pod (up to

15 cm long), pointed at both ends, divided into compartments, and patterned with a network of veins. It contains one to three dark brown seeds with a dull sheen, hard outer covering and deep furrow (1). The seeds are quite large, measuring 3 by 2 by 1.5 cm.

The drug, physostigmine, is exported chiefly from Lagos, Nigeria.

Jaborandi Plant

Pilocarpus jaborandi Holmes

Rutaceae

The approximately 20 species of the genus *Pilocarpus* Wahl are all found in the tropical regions of the Americas. Most widely used by today's pharmaceutical industry are *P. jaborandi* (Pernambuco-Jaborandi), *P. microphyllus* Stapff (Maranham-Jaborandi), *P. pennatifolius* Lemaire (Paraguay-Jaborandi) and *P. racemosus* Wahl (Guadeloupe-Jaborandi). They are mostly native to Brazil but are cultivated in other tropical regions of South America and the Antilles.

The leaves of these shrubs or trees contain the poisonous alkaloids pilocarpine and isopilocarpine in concentrations of 0.2—1 per cent, plus the poisonous auxiliary alkaloids pilocarpidine and pilosine. Pilocarpine is extremely poisonous. The symptoms of poisoning are practically the same as those caused by the Calabar Bean Plant (see *Physostigma venenosum*). Furthermore, pilocarpine causes so much secretion of mucus by the bronchi that the victim is unable to cough it up sufficiently, thereby suffering suffocation, pulmonary oedema and death due to complete exhaustion. The South American Indians use the extract from the leaves for poisoning arrows. Outside the plant's area of distribution, poisoning is caused by excessive doses of medicinal preparations containing pilocarpine.

Modern medicine uses pilocarpine extracted from the dried leaves to stimulate the parasympathetic nerves, to treat retention of urine caused by kidney failure, and in the treatment of oedema. In ophthalmology, it is used, like physostigmine, to contract the pupils and to reduce pressure within the eyeball in the treatment of glaucoma.

The Jaborandi Plant is a shrub approximately 3 m high with branches thickly leaved at the tips and with rust-coloured hairs. The leaves are odd-pinnate with 2—4 pairs of leaflets; the leaflets are leathery and longish-ovate (up to 16 cm long) with an entire margin. The small pentamerous purplish flowers have long stalks (1) and are arranged in a slender raceme up to 40 cm long. The fruits are one-seeded follicles joined in clusters of three to five (2). They burst along the ventral suture ejecting the seeds (3).

P. jaborandi and other species have a relatively distinct area of natural distribution in tropical South America (4).

2

3

1

Betel
Piper betle L.

Piperaceae

The genus *Piper* L. is a very large one, numbering approximately 700 species, all native to the tropical regions of south-east Asia. Some that were cultivated as spices for seasoning foods are now widespread and common in the tropics. The species *P. betle,* sometimes classified in a separate genus *Chavica* Miq., is indigenous to the whole of Malaysia and Indonesia and is also cultivated in southern China, India, the east African coast, Madagascar, Zanzibar, etc. This area of distribution is also the area of betel addiction. The addicts, of whom there are more than 200 million, chew not only the leaves, which are rich in essential oil, but also the so-called 'betel tid-bits'. These are made by coating a fresh betel leaf with a thin layer of mush made from shell lime and wrapping it round a piece of the areca palm-nut (betel nut); to this are added various other aromatic substances according to taste. Chewing liberates a red pigment that stains the saliva and the mouth. Also liberated from the areca palm-nut are the alkaloids arecoline and arecaidine, which produce a feeling of relaxation and well-being.

Betel chewing, like every addiction, has not only pleasant but also adverse effects: in this case, loss of all the teeth due to the immense amount of plaque formed, as well as serious disorders of the digestive system. It also contributes to the risk of cancer of the mouth due to the constant irritation of the mucous lining by the essential oil in the betel leaf, which contains cocarcinogenic components.

A shrubby climbing plant, Betel attains the height of its support. It has thin angled stems covered with alternate entire longish-heart-shaped leaves that are often asymmetrical. The small sessile flowers are densely clustered in long, stalked cylindrical spikes. They have no perianth but are enclosed by a bract and bracteoles. The ovary is superior and globose with a sessile three- to four-lobed stigma and there are two stamens on short thick filaments at the sides. The fruit is a round one-seeded berry resembling a black pepper.

The areca palm-nut (1) is an essential ingredient of the 'betel tid-bit'. It is the fruit of the Betel or Areca-palm *(Areca catechu L.)* which has almost the same

2

154

area of distribution as the Betel Plant.
The nut is about the size of a pigeon's egg
and must therefore be crushed into small
pieces for chewing. The area of betel
chewing (2) is identical to the area of
distribution of the Betel Plant and
Areca-palm.

1

May Apple or Mandrake
Podophyllum peltatum L.

Podophyllum peltatum is native to the Atlantic region of North America, where it grows in shaded, deciduous woods in both the U.S.A. and Canada.

The poisonous components are the lignans podophyllotoxin, alpha-peltatin and beta-peltatin. They are the principal components of the resin podophyllin recovered from the rhizomes for the pharmaceutical industry. The rhizomes are pulverized and extracted with alcohol, followed by the partial concentration of the solution and the addition of acidified water to precipitate the resinous fraction (podophyllin), which is then dried and pulverized. It is light brown or greenish yellow and has a bitter taste. The peltatins have a drastic cathartic action. A small quantity of about 0.01 gm increases the peristaltic movement and secretions of the large intestine; larger quantities act as a strong irritant on the intestines and cause poisoning. Podophyllotoxin is even more toxic. The most common cause of poisoning is excessive dosage. Symptoms are diarrhoea with bloody stools containing also pieces of the intestinal lining and bile, a damaging effect on the action of the heart, profound exhaustion and death due to heart failure. A fatal dose of podophyllin is 0.3—0.5 gm. Poisoning has not been reported in animals, for the above-ground parts of the plant are not poisonous. This age-old medicine of the North American Indians, used against intestinal worms, cancer and as abortive, is today used for medicinal purposes as a component of effective cathartics and medicines stimulating the flow of bile. In recent years, podophyllotoxin has been used in the supplementary post-radiation treatment of cancer for it checks the growth of certain tumours.

May Apple is a perennial herb up to 30 cm high with a long, cylindrical, creeping rhizome approximately 1.5 cm thick. The stem terminates in two stalked opposite shield-shaped leaves divided into five to seven lobes. Between the two leaves is a short-stalked drooping white flower with six sepals and petals, as many as 18 stamens and a superior, unilocular ovary. The fruit is a fleshy yellow berry about the size of a plum (May-apple) with a large number of seeds (1).

The species *P. emodi* Wall. found in Asia from the Himalayas to China and Taiwan, yields the so-called 'Indian podophyllin'. Although three times as much podophyllin can be obtained from the rhizome of this species it is less effective due to the absence of peltatins and more poisonous due to the high concentration of podophyllotoxin (40 per cent).

Angular Solomon's Seal
Polygonatum odoratum (Mill.) Druce

Liliaceae

The genus *Polygonatum* Mill. numbers 30 species found in the northern hemisphere. *P. odoratum* has a Euro-Siberian distribution. It grows in dry open woods, woodland margins and on dry slopes, as a component of original forest-steppe and semi-steppe vegetation. This and other species of *Polygonatum* are grown for decoration as ground cover under trees.

Data pertaining to the poisonous substances found in these plants is contradictory. Earlier data as to the concentration of cardiac glycosides has not been confirmed by current investigation. What has been determined is the presence of saponins, primarily in the rhizomes and berries but also in other parts of the plant. Some authorities state that the sweetish unpleasant-tasting berries contain anthraquinones and believe them to be the cause of poisoning, mostly in children. Symptoms of poisoning are headache, compulsion to urinate, diarrhoea, vomiting, giddiness, and difficulty in breathing. There have been few cases of fatal poisoning but despite this polygonatums must be considered poisonous. Cases of mild poisoning in animals have also been reported.

In folk medicine, both in Europe and elsewhere, e. g. in Japan, the tea from the rhizomes was used to treat diabetes because of its concentration of glucokinins. The rhizomes were also used externally in compresses applied to bruises and internally as a diuretic and for the treatment of rheumatism. Modern medicine does not use these plants.

Angular Solomon's Seal is a perennial herb up to 50 cm high with a creeping branching rhizome and arching stems that are angled and smooth. The leaves are alternate, longish-ovate to lanceolate, the leaves of the lower stem measure 12 by 5 cm and the upper leaves are smaller (3 by 1.5 cm). They are rough, pale green on the upper surface and greyish green on the underside. The flowers, arranged in scanty racemes, grow from the axils of the leaves in May and June. They are drooping, with thin stalks and a white tubular perianth composed of six joined segments. The stamens (three plus three) are united with the flower tube about mid-way down; the ovary is superior and trilocular (1). The fruit is a large, round berry about 1 — 1.5 cm in diameter (2) coloured blue black with a waxy bloom. It contains one to three orbicular slightly flattened wrinkled seeds.

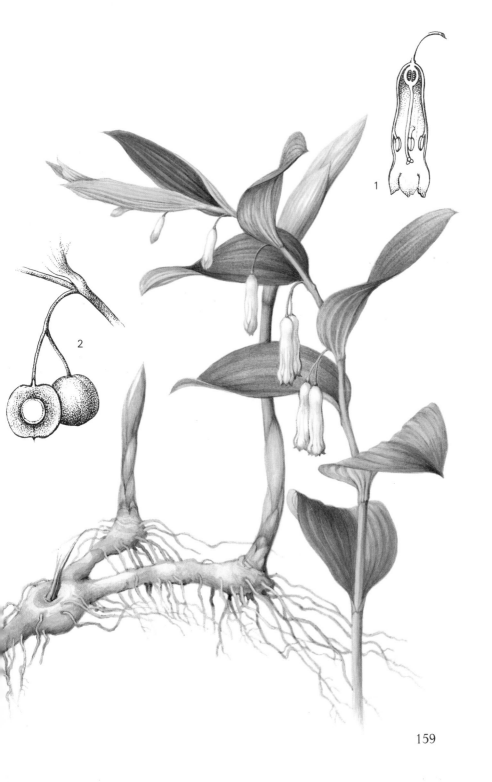

The genus *Primula* L. is one of the largest. It contains more than 500 species, most of them found in the mountains of the northern hemisphere, one important area with a large concentration being the high mountain districts of Asia. The species *P. obconica* is native to the Tibetan region of China, where it grows on the eastern slopes of the Tibetan highlands. It has given rise to a great many cultivated forms of various colours grown for decoration.

Besides the common protoprimulagenin A and priverogenin A and B type saponins, which are poisonous in greater concentrations, and the glycoside primulaverin — all active substances obtained from *P. veris* L. and *P. elatior* (L.) Hill and widely used in modern medicine — *P. obconica* also contains the poisonous irritant primin in the glandular hairs. This is concentrated chiefly in the hairs on the flower stalks and sepals and, in persons who are allergic, it causes severe to blistering inflammation of the skin on contact. Swellings on the face may be accompanied by fever. A mere one-hundredth of a milligram of primin will produce these symptoms. Roughly 20 plants are needed for the recovery of 1 mg of primin. Similar effects are produced also by the related species *P. sinensis* Sab. ex Lindl. and the hybrids of the two, as well as by *P. sieboldii* E. Morren (Japan) and *P. mollis* Nutt. (eastern Himalayas). It is not used in medicine.

1

Primula obconica is a perennial plant with a basal rosette of leaves and is grown for decoration in hothouses in Europe and elsewhere. The leaves are heart-shaped with a toothed margin and glandular hairs. The five-petalled flowers have a white, pink, red or violet corolla and a funnel-shaped calyx that becomes enlarged after the flowers are spent. The ovary is superior, the fruit a capsule.

P. sinensis has lobed leaves and the entire stems covered with sticky hairs. The calyx is enlarged at the base. The flowers are white, pink, to deep red (1). The glandular hairs containing poisonous primin (2) are characteristic of these primulas.

2

Cherry-laurel
Prunus laurocerasus L.

Rosaceae

The large genus *Prunus* L. includes numerous cultivated plants, among them *P. laurocerasus,* found throughout the northern Mediterranean region and to the Caucasus and Iran. In the wild it is characteristically found in mountain forests, chiefly beech woods.

Its leaves contain the cyanogenic glycoside prunasin (Prulaurasin), which on fermentation liberates the extremely poisonous, almond-scented hydrocyanic acid. Similarly, *P. dulcis* (Mill.) R. A. Webb var. *amara* (DC.) Fokke liberates hydrocyanic acid from amygdalin on cleavage. A dose of 50 of the fruits is fatal for adults and ten are fatal for children.

Symptoms of hydrocyanic poisoning are anxiety caused by a feeling of suffocation, headache, shivering, vomiting, faintness, tetanus-like convulsions, paralysis of the respiratory and vasomotor centres and death by suffocation. Hydrocyanic acid is also dangerous to animals for it deprives the tissues of the ability to absorb oxygen from the blood.

P. laurocerasus was used in the nineteenth century to make *Aqua laurocerasi* which is distilled from the crushed leaves that have been steeped in water and contains 0.1 per cent of hydrocyanic acid. It is only rarely used nowadays to suppress coughing, to treat nausea and as a flavouring agent in medicinal preparations.

1 a

This evergreen shrub or tree reaches a height of 3—5 m. The leaves are leathery, glossy on the upper surface, longish-ovate, up to 15 cm long and with a serrated and occasionally revolute margin. The flowering period is April—May. The flowers, arranged in erect racemes 10—15 cm long, have a funnel-shaped hypanthium (a cup-like structure derived from a leaf), five

1 b

caducous sepals, five white petals and
approximately 20 stamens. The fruit is
a globose or ovoid, glossy black drupe
with a smooth, pointed pyrene (1a, 1b).

   P. laurocerasus was brought to Vienna from
Constantinople in 1574 by the botanist
Clusius along with other 'exotic' plants.
The cause of its toxicity was not
determined until the eighteenth century.

Bird Cherry
Prunus padus L.

Rosaceae

Prunus padus has a Euro-Siberian distribution. It is a typical tree of alder groves and shoreline thickets because it requires ground which has a high water table but is not permanently wet. Because it is dispersed by birds, Bird Cherry is often found in places other than its characteristic habitats. Forms with variegated leaves are widely used for decoration in the garden.

Like other members of the genus, Bird Cherry contains the glycosides amygdalin and prulaurasin, which on cleavage liberate poisonous hydrocyanic acid. For this reason, the species must be included in the list of plants dangerous above all for children. The seeds of the globose drupes are not innocuous. When eaten, they soon cause nausea, dryness and a scratchy feeling in the throat, vomiting, difficulty in breathing and, in larger quantities, also cramps. Fatal cases of poisoning are few and far between but they have occurred. Cattle and goats also have been poisoned by grazing on Bird Cherry. The fruit pulp is not poisonous and was formerly used to make home-made jams and juices. The fruit was also distilled to make spirits.

Bird Cherry is not used for medicinal purposes except in homeopathy. In folk medicine, the decoction from the bark was used to stimulate sweating and the flow of urine in the treatment of chills, gout and rheumatism. The decoction from the leaves was likewise used — often causing poisoning — for stomach upsets, as was *Aqua laurocerasi* (see *P. laurocerasus*).

Bird Cherry is a shrub or tree growing to a height of more than 10 m. The twigs are a glossy brownish red with numerous paler lenticels. The leaves are short-stalked, up to 15 cm long, ovate and relatively narrow. They are dark-green on the upper surface and a paler green on the underside. When crushed between the fingers they smell of bitter almonds. Bird Cherry flowers in May and June. The flowers, arranged in dense, drooping racemes nearly 20 cm long, are white and pentamerous. The calyx soon falls, the petals are broadly obovate and up to 1 cm long, and there are approximately 20 stamens (1). The fruit is a glossy black drupe about the size of a pea with a bitter taste (2a, 2b).

164

2a

2b

165

Meadow Buttercup
Ranunculus acris L.

The genus *Ranunculus* L. includes approximately 400 species, many of which grow in cold districts and in the mountains. *R. acris* is a Eurasian species naturalized in America, where it was introduced. It is a typical species of meadow communities and when in flower is the most striking element there.

Like most members of the genus *Ranunculus* and several other genera of the buttercup family, it contains the poisonous glycoside ranunculin which, on cleavage due to the action of the enzyme ranunculase, yields the poisonous protoanemonine and the less poisonous anemonine. Externally, protoanemonine is a strong irritant, causing blistering inflammation of the skin and even ulcers on mucous membranes. Internally, it causes inflammation of the lining of the mouth cavity and of the digestive tract. It causes vomiting, intestinal pains and inflammation of the kidneys; serious poisoning causes giddiness, cramps and death due to respiratory failure. Cattle may be poisoned after grazing on large quantities of the plant but, on the whole, they avoid it unless the growth is particularly lush. Symptoms of poisoning are similar to those mentioned, but relatively few cases are fatal. After grazing in buttercup meadows, milch-cows give bitter, reddish milk. Protoanemonine is broken down and rendered harmless by drying, and thus hay containing the dried plants is not harmful. Protoanemonine is extremely poisonous for fish.

Meadow Buttercup is not used for medicinal purposes except in homeopathy, which recommends the extract for the treatment of gout, rheumatic pains and certain skin diseases.

Meadow Buttercup is a perennial herb found in moist situations and reaching a height of 1 m. The stem is hollow at the base, greatly branched higher up and carrying several flowers. The leaves are simple and palmatifid, the basal leaves long-stalked, the stem leaves short-stalked, and the uppermost leaves sessile with linear segments. The shining golden-yellow flowers, 1—2.5 cm across (depending on the site), are produced from May until September. They have five sepals, five petals, a large number of stamens and superior ovaries. The fruit is an ovate-orbicular achene up to 3 mm long with a short beak (1).

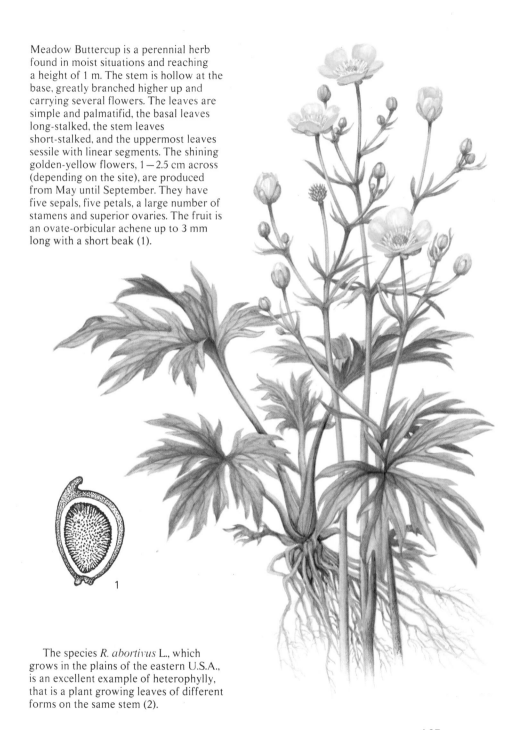

1

The species *R. abortivus* L., which grows in the plains of the eastern U.S.A., is an excellent example of heterophylly, that is a plant growing leaves of different forms on the same stem (2).

167

Lesser Celandine
Ranunculus ficaria L.

Ranunculaceae

Ranunculus ficaria is found in Europe and north Africa, its range extending to central Asia. Its early spring-flowering makes it a striking element in damp meadows, beside streams, in thickets, wet woodlands, alder and oak woods.

In common with many members of the buttercup family, Lesser Celandine is poisonous due to the unstable protoanemonine, derived on cleavage from the glycoside ranunculin. In addition to that, it also contains saponins. Poisoning in humans is relatively rare; the symptoms are similar to those of other species of *Ranunculus* (see *Ranunculus acris*). Cases of poisoning have been caused by the eating of so-called spring salad made from the young leaves and by eating the pickled buds as a substitute for capers. Animals are not often poisoned, only when grazing in meadows where Lesser Celandine occurs in great masses. Poisoning in cattle, sheep and goats causes diarrhoea, inflammation of the kidneys, cramps and, in fatal instances, respiratory failure. Drying renders the plant harmless and therefore hay containing it is not harmful.

Lesser Celandine is no longer used for medicinal purposes except in homeopathy, which recommends the essence from the fresh top parts for treating haemorrhoids. In folk medicine it is used in spring 'blood-cleansing' cures and, externally, in bath preparations for haemorrhoids and eczemas.

2

A perennial herb less than 20 cm high, Lesser Celandine has a short rhizome, tuberous roots and ascending stems that sometimes root. The leaves are heart-shaped with a shallow cleft at the base. There are tiny bulbils in the axils of the leaves. The flowering period is March–April. The golden-yellow flowers, with 8–12 petals, numerous stamens and superior ovaries, measure 2–3 cm in diameter. The fruit is an achene (1a, 1b) that rarely develops, which is why Lesser Celandine multiplies mainly vegetatively, either by means of the bulbils in the leaf axils or by root tubers.

The widely cultivated Winter Aconite, *Eranthis hyemalis* (L.) Salisb. (2), likewise of the buttercup family, is also poisonous. It is native to southern Europe, flowers in late winter or early spring and has bright yellow sepals. It contains cardiac glycosides similar to those of Spring Pheasant's Eye (see *Adonis vernalis*).

Creeping Buttercup
Ranunculus repens L.

Ranunculaceae

The Eurasian species *Ranunculus repens* has a widespread distribution. It is a weedy plant noteworthy for its marked variability and adaptability, ranging from aquatic to dry land forms. It is a pioneering plant, being one of the first to occupy waste places, rubbish tips and dumps. It spreads and multiplies chiefly vegetatively, by means of its long, creeping runners, which root rapidly and firmly, forming large masses in meadows and gardens that are difficult to eradicate.

The toxicity of this buttercup is similar to that of the species *R. acris*. It is sometimes added by mistake, along with the most highly poisonous member of this genus *(R. sceleratus* L.), to commercially-grown leaf vegetables for both species grow mainly as weeds among cultivated garden vegetables. On record are cases of poisoning caused, for example, by frozen spinach containing these plants, for their toxicity was not destroyed by this method of food processing. Children have been known to suffer conjunctivitis on rubbing their eyes with their hands after picking the flowers.

The South African species *R. capensis* Thunb. and *R. pinnatus* Poir. are used by the Africans to treat diseases of the urinary passages and cancer.

Buttercups are not used for medicinal purposes except in eastern phytotherapy.

Creeping Buttercup is a low perennial herb, approximately 30 cm high, with thick fibrous roots and leafy creeping runners that root at the nodes. The basal leaves are trifoliolate and stalked. The flowering stem is practically leafless. The flowers, borne between May and August, are golden-yellow and up to 3 cm across. The achenes are orbicular and slightly flattened with a short three-sided beak.

The shape of the achenes is an important means of identification in some species e. g. the achenes of *R. arvensis* L. (1), *R. bulbosus* L. (2) and *R . repens* L. (3).

Common Buckthorn
Rhamnus cathartica L.

The genus *Rhamnus* L. numbers some 150 species found chiefly in the temperate regions of the northern hemisphere. *R. cathartica* is a native of central and southern Europe, its range extending from Siberia to north Africa. It grows in wet woods, oak woods and scrub, from lowland to hilly districts. It is used, along with other species of *Rhamnus,* by the pharmaceutical industry for its cathartic properties.

It contains anthracene glycosides, the greatest concentration being in the seeds, with less in the bark. In therapeutic doses they act as a cathartic. Because the action is exerted in the large intestine, the effect is neither immediate nor rapid; that is why poisoning occurs in people who are impatient and take excessive amounts in their desire for prompt results. The symptoms of poisoning are severe diarrhoea with bloody stools and vomiting accompanied by fever. Animals are not often poisoned as they find the plant's odious bitter taste unpalatable.

Active principles of the same type are to be found in the related Alder Buckthorn *(R. frangula L.),* which has a similar geographic distribution. In this case, vomiting is caused by the anthracene glycosides in the fresh bark, which must be stored for at least one year before these poisonous substances change into effective and non-poisonous glucofrangulins and frangulins. In the U.S.A., it is chiefly the bark of the species *R. purshiana* DC., containing cathartic aloin-type and cascaroside-type anthracene derivatives, which is used for medicinal purposes. Excessive quantities, however, produce undesirable symptoms of poisoning.

Common Buckthorn grows into a spreading shrub up to 3 m high and, very occasionally, a small tree. The branches bear opposite twigs terminating

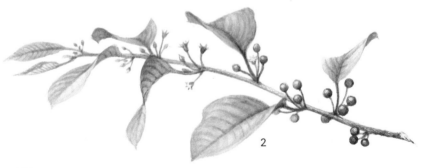

2

in thorns. The leaves are simple, firm and leathery, of varied shape and with a notched or toothed margin; on older twigs they grow in clusters. The insignificant flowers, borne in May and June, are four-petalled, greenish and fragrant. They are arranged in clusters in axillary cymes. The calyx is joined at the base into a hypanthium. The fruit is a black, globose drupe, larger than a pea, with two to four woody one-seeded pyrenes (1). The species *R. frangula* (2) is also a shrub. The flowers are five-partite and yellow-green. The drupes are three-seeded and coloured blackish violet.

1

173

Alpine Rose
Rhododendron ferrugineum L.

The genus *Rhododendron* L. in the broader term embraces a total of 1300 species, their centres of origin located in the mountains of central and east Asia and the temperate regions of North America, extending into the Arctic region. Only six species are native to Europe; there are none in Australia and Africa. *R. ferrugineum* grows in acidic soils in the Alps (hence the name Alpine Rose) on the colder damp northern flanks, where it may be found also in rock crevices up to elevations of more than 2000 m.

Rhododendrons and azaleas are among the loveliest of ornamental shrubs for park, garden and room decoration. Breeding and selection has produced a large number of cultivated varieties including miniature forms for the rock garden.

Rhododendrons contain the poisonous diterpene andromedotoxin, which lowers the blood pressure for a long period and affects the action of the heart. Even the honey from bees visiting these plants contains this poisonous substance. Most species of rhododendron are definitely poisonous. Cases of poisoning, however, are rare; they occur when excessive quantities are taken as a home remedy or honey containing andromedotoxin is eaten. The symptoms of poisoning are a burning sensation in the mouth, extreme salivation, vomiting, diarrhoea and a cold sweat, difficulty in swallowing and speaking, a slowed heartbeat, barely perceptible pulse, difficulty in breathing, coma, and death due to respiratory failure.

In Europa, Asia and America sheep, goats, cattle and horses have been poisoned after feeding on widely varied species of azaleas and rhododendrons.

The Alpine Rose is a slow-growing thickly-branched evergreen shrub up to 1 m high. The leaves are leathery and glossy dark green on the upper surface; the underside of the leaves and young shoots are covered with rusty-brown glands. Alpine Rose flowers from May until the summer, depending on the location and altitude. The blossoms, arranged in terminal clusters of 3–10 flowers, are pentamerous and coloured deep red. The ovary is superior and five-locular (1). The fruit is a capsule (2), dehiscing by five valves and containing minute seeds — among the smallest and lightest of all seeds in the plant realm. The yellow-flowering, deciduous azaleas (*R. luteum* Sweet) are sometimes placed in a separate genus: *Azalea* L. *Kalmia latifolia* L. (3), an ornamental shrub native to North America and which grows wild in the Appalachian mountains, is closely related to rhododendrons. It, too, contains the poisonous andromedotoxin and animals have often suffered poisoning as a result.

2

1

3

Castor-oil Plant
Ricinus communis L.

Euphorbiaceae

Ricinus communis is probably native to Africa and Asia but spread by cultivation to tropical and sub-tropical regions throughout the world. It has been grown since time immemorial for its oil, formerly used for lighting and as a medicine. Nowadays, it is an indispensable non-drying lubricant for high-speed machines. Every year 500 000 — 800 000 tonnes of oil are produced from the seeds mostly in Brazil, India, the former U.S.S.R., Thailand and the African countries.

The poisonous component of castor-oil seeds is primarily the phytotoxin ricin, an extremely toxic protein. It is the most toxic of all natural poisons — a mere 0.25 mg is fatal. Ricin does not break down in the organism but is absorbed as such and, because it inhibits the synthesis of proteins, it disrupts vital metabolic processes in the body. Ten seeds are a fatal dose for adults and 2—3 seeds are enough to kill a child. The action of the poison is slow; symptoms appear after ten hours or even more and then it is too late to save the victim. Symptoms of poisoning are vomiting, diarrhoea, a cold sweat, a burning sensation in the mouth, thirst, cyanosis (bluish coloration of the skin), heart disorders, convulsions, and death due to respiratory failure and cardiac arrest. Children may be poisoned by mistaking the seeds for the harmless beans that they resemble. Animals tolerate relatively greater quantities than man. Nevertheless, cases of poisoning, some of them fatal, have been reported when animals were fed crushed castor-beans which have not been properly processed.

The oil is used in medicine as a reliable cathartic. A dose of 15—30 gm for adults takes effect in 2—4 hours. It is also used in the cosmetic industry.

The Castor-oil Plant is grown as an annual in temperate regions. In the tropics, it is cultivated as a perennial plant that often attains the proportions of a large shrub or tree 10—12 m high. The leaves are large, stalked, palmately divided and have a toothed margin. The monoecious flowers are arranged in panicles, with male flowers at the bottom and female flowers at the top. The male flowers have a yellow-green perianth enclosing a large number of branched stamens (1), the female flowers a greenish perianth that soon falls, a superior trilocular ovary and red bifid stigmas (2). The fruit is an ovoid or globose capsule, with or without spines (3a, 3b). The seeds are longish-ovoid, slightly flattened, marbled (4) and of varied shape, size and colour depending on the variety.

176

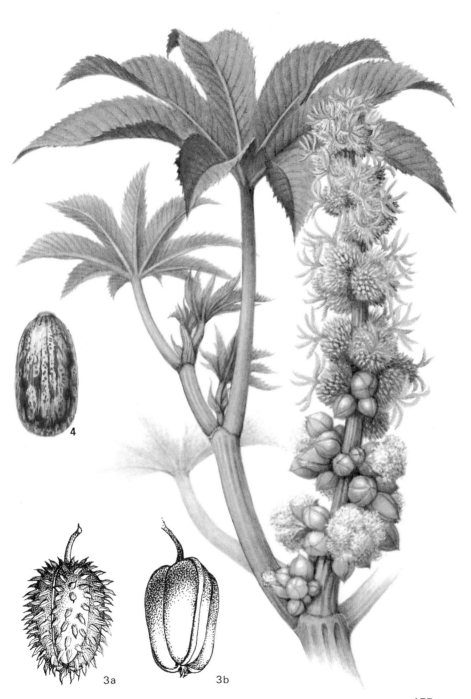

3a

3b

4

Rue
Ruta graveolens L.

The centre of distribution of the species *Ruta graveolens* is southern and south-eastern Europe. Rue grows wild in the karst districts of the Mediterranean region, often as a naturalized escape from cultivated plantings, for it has been grown as a culinary and medicinal herb since ancient times.

Certain components of the essential oil, mainly ketones, are poisonous as are furocoumarins which are found in the top parts of the plant. Various coumarins also are suspected of being poisonous: the coumarin glycoside rutarin (marmesin) and recently isolated acridine alkaloids such as gravacridondiole. The essential oil as well as the furocoumarins are skin irritants. Many people cannot pick Rue without wearing gloves as their hands and face swell and develop a rash and blisters, which is often accompanied by fever. These symptoms are dangerous in susceptible children, who are liable to suffer long-term effects. When using Rue, either in the form of an extract or infusion, incorrect dosage may cause inflammation of the lining of the mouth cavity and digestive tract accompanied by vomiting, diarrhoea and a feeling of general weakness sometimes ending in collapse. Inflammation of the kidneys and liver damage in cases of more severe poisoning are extremely dangerous. Pregnant women may abort due to congestion of the lower pelvic region; such cases have often been fatal when Rue was administered as a home remedy. As a result of recent research, Rue may be used for new purposes in the treatment of disorders of the autonomic nervous system, and it continues to be used in the food industry (in small amounts) as a seasoning.

2

A perennial, aromatic herb, Rue sometimes grows into a small shrub up to 80 cm high with a woody base. The leaves are bi- to trifoliolate, very decorative yellow-green on the upper surface, with a bluish bloom on the underside. The flowering period is from June until August. The dense inflorescence is composed of pentamerous flowers at the top and

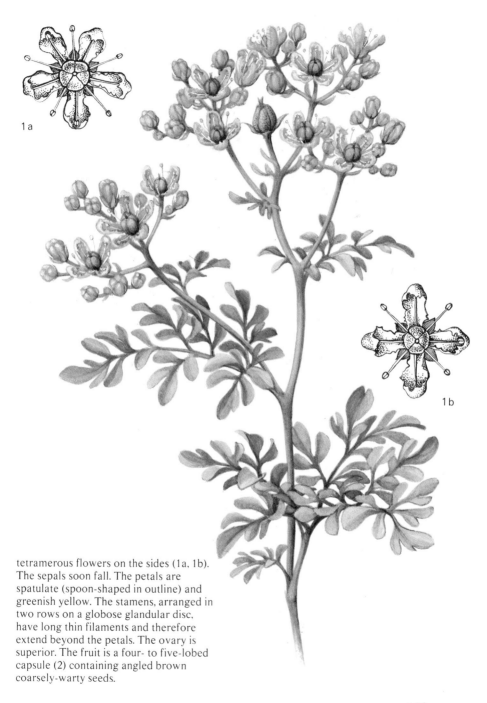

1a

1b

tetramerous flowers on the sides (1a, 1b).
The sepals soon fall. The petals are
spatulate (spoon-shaped in outline) and
greenish yellow. The stamens, arranged in
two rows on a globose glandular disc,
have long thin filaments and therefore
extend beyond the petals. The ovary is
superior. The fruit is a four- to five-lobed
capsule (2) containing angled brown
coarsely-warty seeds.

The genus *Scopolia* Jacq.corr.Link includes only four species native to the temperate regions of Eurasia. *S. carniolica* is native to the eastern Alps and eastern Carpathians, and has been introduced further east. It grows in shaded broad-leaved woods, ravines and valleys, at high altitudes.

The roots contain poisonous tropane alkaloids, primarily L-hyoscyamine. Their proportion is similar to the alkaloids in Deadly Nightshade (see *Atropa bella-donna*). Poisoning may be caused by ignorance or, as was done mainly in the Carpathians, criminal intent. The symptoms of poisoning are the same as for Deadly Nightshade.

Domestic animals are not often poisoned by Scopolia, it has occurred only in young animals and in cattle fed hay containing this plant. The dried root was formerly used in medicine as the equivalent of and substitute for belladonna root to relieve spasms. It is still grown today for the recovery of L-hyoscyamine.

In folk medicine, it was used primarily in the late Middle Ages as a narcotic agent and ingredient of love potions, a practice that usually ended in death by poisoning.

1

Scopolia is a perennial herb up to 50 cm high with a thick rhizome and a thick forked stem. The dingy green leaves are alternate, ovate, with an entire margin and measuring up to 18 by 9 cm. The flowering period is from April until June. The solitary flowers resemble those of Thorn-apple (see *Datura stramonium*). They are long-stalked, drooping, up to 3 cm long and 1.5 cm wide. The tubular

bell-shaped corolla is brownish purplish
green outside and olive green within. The
round capsule opens by a lid. The seeds
are brown, 3—4 mm long and knobbly.

First described by P. A. Matthioli in
1558, Scopolia soon became an important
drug in Renaissance apothecaries as
illustrated by this majolica apothecary's
jar made in Holland (1).

Common Stonecrop or Wall-pepper
Sedum acre L.

Crassulaceae

The genus *Sedum* L. includes approximately 500 species found mainly in the northern hemisphére with centres of origin in the Himalayas, eastern Asia and Mexico. *S. acre* is a native of Europe, north Africa and Asia as far as the Altai. It grows in dry and sunny situations, on walls, screes and rocks. Sedums are very popular rock garden plants and breeding and selection have produced a great many cultivated forms.

Metabolites found in sedums include specific types of organic acids (isocitric acid) and sugars (seduheptulosa), and the various alkaloids are also an indication of a special type of metabolism. All the identified alkaloids are poisonous; the principal ones have been named isopelletierine, sedridine, sedamine and sedinine. Their concentration is by no means small — 0.27 per cent. The content of the various alkaloids may vary and the possibility of there being certain chemical races within the species cannot be excluded. The alkaloids have a local irritant action and dilate the pupils. When ingested, they cause vomiting, stupor, paralysis and, in extreme cases, respiratory failure. Sedum poisoning, however, is not common in humans or animals.

Detailed pharmaceutical research is lacking; results to date indicate that the drug lowers blood pressure. Homeopathy uses Sedum to check haemorrhoidal bleeding. Folk medicine recommends the decoction for epilepsy and as an abortive. Its toxicity, however, makes its use dangerous.

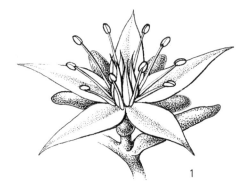

1

Common Stonecrop is a fleshy-leaved creeping perennial approximately 10 cm high. It has a thin but much-branched rhizome and ascending stems. The latter are of two types: non-flowering stems densely covered with fleshy overlapping 3—10 mm long leaves, and flowering stems which are less densely leaved and carry a scanty inflorescence. All parts of the plant have a sharp, burning taste. The flowering period is from May until August. The flowers are short-stalked and pentamerous. The sepals are approximately 3 mm long; the pale yellow petals are 6—10 mm long. There are ten stamens and the ovary is superior (1). The fruit is a pointed follicle 3—5 mm long; it splits open in rainy weather and the fine minute seeds are washed out by the rain.

Common Ragwort
Senecio jacobaea L.

Compositae

The genus *Senecio* L. numbers more than 1500 species distributed throughout the world and exhibiting diverse morphological and ecological characteristics. *S. jacobaea* has a Euro-Siberian distribution extending southward to north Africa. It is common in pastureland and meadows, on slopes and in woodlands.

   S. jacobaea contains poisonous pyrrolizidine alkaloids that are carcinogenic and primarily cause serious liver damage (necrosis and cirrhosis). Other poisonous components are the retronecin esters, e. g. retrorsin, isatidin and senecionin. Cattle and horses that graze on ragwort suffer chronic poisoning, which causes poor digestion, hepatitis, blindness, a faltering gait and finally collapse. In central Europe, horses are affected by a serious disease after grazing on other species of ragwort: *S. barbareifolius* (Wimm. et Grab.) Berger and *S. aquaticus* Huds. A similar disease, called Molteno disease, causing liver disorders in horses and cattle has been described in South Africa. It occurs when the animals have grazed on local ragworts, which include a great many species. Similar diseases (Winton disease and Pictou disease) described in New Zealand and Australia are likewise caused by feeding on ragwort.

   Ragworts and their alkaloids are not used for medicinal purposes as yet, except in homeopathic treatment of intestinal worms and gynaecological diseases. However, the possibility of their use in medicine after they have been subjected to more detailed pharmaceutical research cannot be excluded.

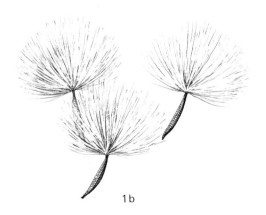

1 b

1 a

Common Ragwort is a biennial or perennial herb reaching a height of 80 cm. The stem is brownish red, sharply grooved, and branched at the top to form a dense corymbose panicle. The basal leaves are lyrate, the stem leaves pinnatipartite. When the plant flowers (from June until September) the basal leaves have usually died down. The yellow flowerheads measure 1.5—2 cm in diameter. They are composed of up to 15 ray flowers and as many as 80 disc flowers. The ray flowers (up to 1 cm long) are expanded and curve downwards after pollination. The fruit is a cylindrical achene with a pappus twice its length that falls readily (1a, 1b).

Bittersweet or Woody Nightshade
Solanum dulcamara L.

Solanaceae

The genus *Solanum* L. embraces more than 1500 species found mainly in sub-tropical regions throughout the world. The majority, however, is native to South and Central America. *S. dulcamara* is a Eurasian species found in wet woods and on the seashore as well as near human habitation.

Like many other members of this genus, it contains steroid glycoalkaloids and saponins. The roots contain as many as eight alkamines (soladulcidine, solasodine, tomatidine, and others) whereas there is usually only one, soladulcine, in the top parts. The fruits are most poisonous before they mature; when ripe they contain only neutral, less poisonous saponins. Children have been poisoned after eating 6–8 green berries. Symptoms of poisoning are nausea and vomiting, diarrhoea, a marked drop in the number of red blood corpuscles, a feeling of general weakness, paralysis of the tongue, difficulty in swallowing and breathing and, very occasionally, death due to respiratory failure and cardiac arrest. Domestic animals have exhibited symptoms of poisoning accompanied by digestive disorders after grazing on the plant but no deaths have been recorded. Similar symptoms are produced by the related species *S. nigrum* L. In fact, the top parts of potato and tomato plants are poisonous and dangerous if fed to animals because of the concentration of alkaloids and saponins in their tissues.

S. dulcamara is no longer used in medicine nor as a home remedy. However, the use of this and other species of *Solanum* for the production of steroid medicines is still being considered.

A perennial herb that becomes woody at the base, Bittersweet has a prostrate or climbing stem up to 2 m long. The leaves are longish-ovate, the upper leaves sagittate. The flowers, which are produced from June until August, are arranged in lateral, usually drooping cymes. They are pentamerous with a persistent calyx, a violet corolla that has reflexed pointed petals, stamens inclined towards the centre of the flower, and a superior ovary. The fruit is a drooping

ovoid glossy red berry with lentil-shaped seeds.

The Solanaceae family also includes the Mandrake (*Mandragora officinarum* L.) native to southern Europe (1). It was believed to have magical powers because the root was thought to resemble the human form and shriek when plucked from the ground. It is a poisonous plant containing tropane alkaloids which give it emetic and narcotic properties. It is only of historic interest nowadays.

Strophanthus hispidus DC.

The genus *Strophanthus* DC., native to the tropical regions of equatorial Africa, Asia and Malaysia, includes approximately 50 species. The species *S. hispidus* is indigenous to the west coast of tropical Africa from Senegal to Sierra Leone. Its seed has been an official drug in most west-European countries, the U.S.A. and South America since 1886. The species *S. kombé* Oliv., native to south-east Africa from Zambia north to lake Victoria, is likewise an official drug in most European countries, in the U.S.A. and Japan. The seed of *S. gratus* (Wall. et Hook. ex Benth.) Baill., found in tropical west Africa south of Sierra Leone to Angola, was formerly an official drug only in Germany. Now, a century later, these two species *S. gratus* and *S. kombé* have become a focus of interest to the pharmaceutical industry and medicine.

All species contain strophanthins, extremely poisonous cardiac glycosides found mainly in the seeds in concentrations of 3.5—8 per cent; the most important ones are g-strophanthin (Ouabain) and k-strophanthin. These are cardinal cardiac medicines used as heart stimulants in acute cases. They must be administered in the form of injections; they are absorbed poorly if taken by mouth. Poisoning is caused only if strophanthin is administered in excessive quantities and in fatal instances (0.005 gm is already a fatal dose) ends in convulsions and death due to cardiac arrest. The extract from the seeds, fruits, bark and roots has been used for ages past by African tribes to make lethal poison arrows.

2

A woody vine with decussate, ovate-elliptical leaves, *Strophanus hispidus* climbs even the towering trees of the tropics. The entire plant is covered with stiff, pale yellow hairs. The flowers are pentamerous and very striking being white with red spots inside. The calyx is funnel-shaped, the petals long (up to 20 cm in length), linear and erect, later drooping. The fruits are two capsules

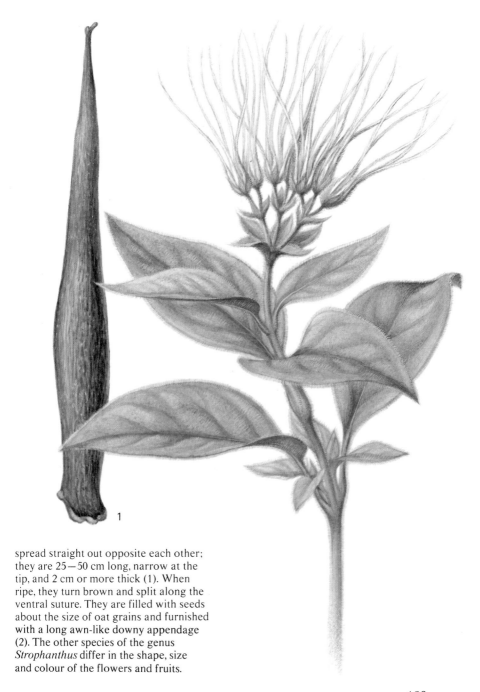

1

spread straight out opposite each other;
they are 25—50 cm long, narrow at the
tip, and 2 cm or more thick (1). When
ripe, they turn brown and split along the
ventral suture. They are filled with seeds
about the size of oat grains and furnished
with a long awn-like downy appendage
(2). The other species of the genus
Strophanthus differ in the shape, size
and colour of the flowers and fruits.

189

Nux Vomica
Strychnos nux-vomica L.

Loganiaceae

Strychnos nux-vomica is native to India and south-east Asia where it grows in the tropical rain forests. It is also naturalized elsewhere, e.g. in Sri Lanka, Malaysia and northern Australia.

All parts of the plant are poisonous. The leaves contain 2 per cent, the bark 8 per cent, and the seeds 2—3 per cent of indole alkaloids, primarily the extremely poisonous strychnine, plus brucine, vomicine, colubrine and other alkaloids. The fatal dose of strychnine for adults is 0.02—0.03 gm. Brucine is up to 50 times less toxic. Like strychnine, it is extremely bitter and is used as a standard (a basis of comparison) in measuring bitterness. Poisoning is caused by mistake, by excessive dosage or by criminal intent. Strychnine is a convulsant poison. Symptoms are a stiffening of the facial and neck muscles, a feeling of suffocation, livid features and convulsions. After several convulsions, the victim dies, fully conscious, by asphyxia due to paralysis of the respiratory centre.

Strychnine was formerly widely used as a vermin killer, which often led to cattle poisoning through carelessness. In the tropics, the extract from various parts of the plant is used by the aborigines to make poison arrows. In Europe, strychnine was used as a poison from the fifteenth century onwards. It was only later used in medicine. In small quantities, it improves muscular function, respiration and circulation. Its compounds, strychnine acid and strychnine oxide, are used therefore as an analeptic (restorative medicine) and as a tonic.

1b

A shrub or tree up to 15 m high, Nux Vomica has opposite, broadly-ovate glossy leathery leaves. The small white pentamerous flowers, with a corolla approximately 1 cm long, are arranged in a cymose inflorescence. There are five stamens and a superior, ovoid ovary. The fruit is a round berry, resembling a small orange in shape and colour (1a, 1b), with white, gel-like pulp in which are embedded several (three to eight) round flat disc-like seeds coloured a glossy yellow-green (2).

The highly poisonous curare used by South American Indians to make poison arrows is a thickened solid extract prepared from various species of the genus *Strychnos* and *Chondrodendron* found in the South American tropics. These are primarily *S. toxifera* Benth., *S. castelnaei* Wedell and *S. crevauxii* G. Planch. The arrow poison is carried by the Indians in bamboo stems, earthenware bowls or calabashes (3a, 3b).

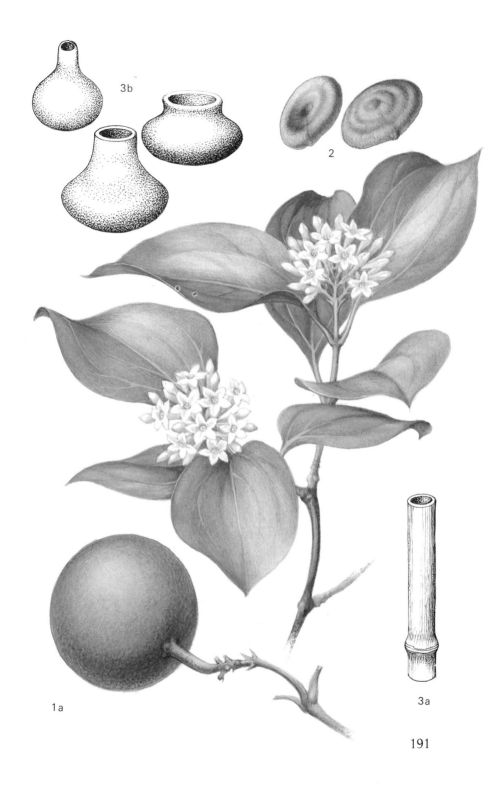

3b

2

1a

3a

191

Common or **English Yew**
Taxus baccata L.

Taxaceae

Taxus baccata has a Euro-oriental distribution extending to northern Iran. It is found also in the mountain districts of the Mediterranean region. At one time common and widespread, its numbers were greatly decimated by felling in the Middle Ages, and today it is used for decoration in parks and gardens. The remaining natural stands are rigidly protected by law wherever they occur.

All parts, except the fleshy aril, are poisonous. They contain the highly poisonous alkaloid taxin, a small amount of auxiliary alkaloids and the glycoside taxicatin. The needles contain the greatest concentration of taxin in winter (2 per cent) and the least concentration in summer (0.5 per cent). The seeds contain approximately 1 per cent. The decoction from just 50—100 gm of needles or a mere 30 'berries' is fatal for an adult. The most likely to be poisoned are children, who may chew the young shoots or the seeds in the fleshy arils. The action of the poison is extremely rapid because taxin is quickly absorbed in the digestive system. It is a very poisonous cardiovascular toxic substance and causes vomiting and abdominal pains, painful diarrhoea, dilated pupils, pallor, collapse, cramps, unconsciousness, and death due to cardiac arrest and respiratory failure often within an hour following ingestion. Horses are the most susceptible of the animals and may die within several minutes of feeding on the young shoots. The literature states that 100—200 gm of the needles is a fatal dose for a horse. Pigs are also susceptible, but a five-fold amount is required to poison cattle.

Yew is not used for medicinal purposes.

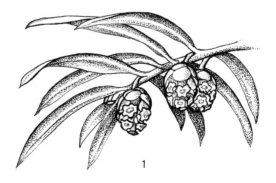

1

2

This is a coniferous tree (5−10 m high) or a large bushy shrub (2−3 m high) with deep roots and a slow rate of growth. There is no resin either in the wood or in the needles. The leaves are soft, flat and needle-like, dark green above and pale green on the underside. The Yew does not begin to produce flowers until after more than ten years. It is dioecious and the flowers are formed in the autumn.

The male flowers are arranged in small globose heads (1); the female flowers resemble buds. The stamens produce large quantities of pollen (Yew is wind pollinated). The female flowers have a single ovule which develops into a single seed enveloped by a fleshy scarlet cup-like aril (2). The seeds are dispersed by birds.

193

Poison Sumac
Toxicodendron quercifolium (Michx.) Greene

Anacardiaceae

Toxicodendron quercifolium (Rhus toxicodendron L.) is native to the U.S.A. and southern Canada. It grows in dry rocky places, on pasture-land and waste ground. Unlike other sumacs, which yield varnish, Japan wax and tannin, this species has no other use except as an ornamental shrub.

The latex contains the poisonous pyrocatechin derivatives hydro-urushiol and hydrolaccol, the mono-olefin urushenol and the poly-phenol fisetin which cause severe dermatitis. Allergic reactions appear immediately on contact with the latex. An itching red patch and blisters occur on the skin within the area of contact, followed by scabs when the blisters burst. Even the small amount of 0.001 mg causes a rash. Accompanying symptoms are nausea and fever. Accidental ingestion of the plant causes giddiness, delirium, and later inflammation of the digestive tract and kidneys. Poisoning is not fatal, as a rule, but the after-effects last a long time. Animals that have eaten sumac suffer diarrhoea and inflammation of the digestive tract, often ending in death.

Other highly poisonous and extremely dangerous sumacs are *T. verniciflua* (Stokes) Barkl. and *T. vernix* (L.) O. Kuntze, both sources of excellent natural varnishes.

Sumacs are not used for medicinal purposes.

2

1a

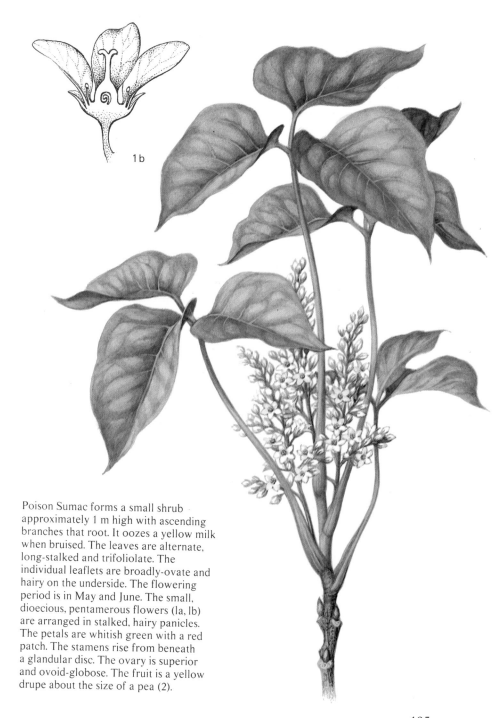

1b

Poison Sumac forms a small shrub
approximately 1 m high with ascending
branches that root. It oozes a yellow milk
when bruised. The leaves are alternate,
long-stalked and trifoliolate. The
individual leaflets are broadly-ovate and
hairy on the underside. The flowering
period is in May and June. The small,
dioecious, pentamerous flowers (la, lb)
are arranged in stalked, hairy panicles.
The petals are whitish green with a red
patch. The stamens rise from beneath
a glandular disc. The ovary is superior
and ovoid-globose. The fruit is a yellow
drupe about the size of a pea (2).

195

Globe Flower
Trollius europaeus L.

The genus *Trollius* L. numbers approximately 25 species native to the temperate regions of the northern hemisphere up to the arctic zone. *T. europaeus* is a native of Europe (in the south it grows only in the mountains), its range extending to western Siberia and the southern Arctic. It is a typical species of sub-montane and mountain meadows. Some ornamental forms and their hybrids are grown in rock gardens.

Globe Flower contains the poisonous alkaloid magnofloria (not berberin as is often stated) and complementary isoquinoline bases. It also contains saponins not precisely determined as yet. It does not contain the glycoside ranunculin and the protoanemonine derived from it. Therefore, Globe Flower's toxicity is different from other members of the Ranunculaceae family. It is not a local irritant. Taken internally, it causes a feeling of excitement at first, followed by stupor, difficulty in breathing, a weak pulse, cold sweat, nausea, vomiting and irritation of the urinary passages. The symptoms of poisoning resemble those of nicotine poisoning. There is no record of human or animal poisoning that has ended in death.

Globe Flower is not used in medicine and only occasionally serves as a home remedy for unspecified ailments.

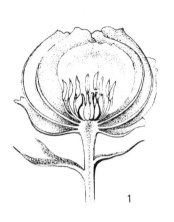

This perennial herb has a simple stem up to 70 cm high. The leaves are palmately divided into five segments, each of which is divided into three parts. The bottom leaves are long-stalked; the top leaves are smaller and sessile. The flowering period varies from May until August depending on the locality; it is earliest in the foothills and latest up in the mountains. The solitary deep yellow flowers are globular and up to 3 cm in diameter (1). The calyx is composed of 5—15 yellow segments arranged in a globe-like cluster. The 5—10 petals are deep-yellow linear segments, modified into nectaries enclosed by the calyx. There are a great many stamens and ovaries. The fruit is a slightly crooked many-seeded short-beaked follicle up to 1.2 cm long (2). The seeds are glossy black and approximately 1.5 mm long.

2

197

Sea Squill or Sea Onion
Urginea maritima (L.) Baker

Urginea maritima is a typical species of the Mediterranean region. It grows chiefly along the coast on dry hills in maquis and at the edges of olive groves, but it is also often found far inland. It occurs as two varieties — one white, the other red — that differ in the colour of the bulb and of the keel of the perianth segments. The white variety is the more common on the European coast and the red on the African coast. Sea Squill is an important pharmaceutical and rodenticide.

Its poisonous constituents are cardiac glycosides of the bufodienolid group, namely scillaren A and several other glycosides formerly called scillaren B. The principal glycoside of the red variety is scillirosid, which besides having a strong effect on the heart also has toxic properties specifically affecting rats and other harmful rodents. Poisoning, when it does happen, is usually due to overdosage during medicinal therapy; in fatal instances, death is due to cardiac arrest. Typical symptoms are digestive and visual disorders and cardiac weakness.

Because of their powerful rodenticidal properties and non-effect on pigs and cattle, preparations from the red variety are used to kill rats in farm buildings. They do not affect the heart as much as the central nervous system. Medicaments from Sea Squill are of great importance in present-day medicine.

The plant is a perennial with a bulb often as large as an infant's head and weighing several kilograms. The bulb of the white variety is greenish white inside with occasional reddish violet cells whereas the red variety is reddish violet due to the presence of anthocyanin (a reddish blue pigment) and tannins (phlobatannin) (1). The leaves (15—20) appear after the flowers have faded, either in the autumn or in spring. They are broadly lanceolate (50 by 8 cm) and dry up in summer. At this time the bulb bears a scape up to 150 cm long with flowers arranged in a dense raceme at the top. The perianth segments are whitish flushed with green or purplish green on the keel. The fruit is a globose, loculisect capsule filled with compressed flat black seeds.

1

Common White Hellebore
Veratrum album L.

The genus *Veratrum* L. includes approximately 50 species distributed in the northern hemisphere. Best known in Europe is *V. album,* which has a wide Euro-Siberian distribution. It occurs only in mountainous areas from the Pyrenees, through the Alps, Carpathian, Caucasus and Scandinavian mountain ranges to the Urals, Altai, Siberia and the Far East, where it grows in damp mountain meadows up to the alpine zone. It is an important pharmaceutical plant. The rhizome and roots yield a drug used for the commercial recovery of alkaloids.

All species of hellebore and all parts of the plant are poisonous. The greatest concentration of poisonous alkaloids is in the rhizomes and roots (1—1.6 per cent). Most effective are protoveratrine A and B, germerine and germitrine. A fatal dose for adults is 10—30 mg of alkaloids, or 1—2 gm of the drug. Death occurs due to respiratory failure and cardiac arrest following a sudden drop in blood pressure. Externally, the drug as well as the pure alkaloids have a strong irritant effect (sneezing, a burning sensation in, and watering of, the eyes, increased salivation). Animals are rarely poisoned because they avoid hellebore when grazing. Nevertheless horses, cattle (chiefly calves) as well as sheep have been fatally poisoned after being fed hay from mountain meadows containing hellebore.

The drug is used in medicine only for specific treatment of high blood pressure. It is more widely used in veterinary medicine, internally for digestive disorders and externally for troublesome parasites.

The large, perennial Common White Hellebore grows up to 150 cm high from a short stout rhizome with a large number of roots. The leaves are broadly elliptical (30 by 12 cm) and furrowed, with prominent venation. The flowering period is from June until August. The flowering stem, produced once in several years, is stout and leafy and covered with soft hairs at the top. The leaves cover the stem up to the inflorescence where they are supplanted by bracts. The inflorescence, composed of racemes, is panicle-like and up to 50 cm long or longer. The flowers at the bottom of the panicle are hermaphroditic and female; those at the top are male. The perianth is either white or greenish, depending on

2

1

whether the plant belongs to the
sub-species *albicans* or *lobelianum*. The
fruit is a capsule composed of three
follicles (1) splitting along the ventral
suture. The seeds are compressed, flat,
pale brown and winged (2).

Lesser Periwinkle
Vinca minor L.

The centre of origin of the herb *Vinca minor* is southern and central Europe but the plant spread through cultivation and is now distributed throughout practically the whole of Europe, growing scattered in oak and oak-hornbeam woods. Until recently, it was used only as an ornamental for edging, but nowadays it is also important as a drug for the pharmaceutical industry.

It contains numerous indole alkaloids, principally vincamine, which have medicinal properties in therapeutic doses but are poisonous in larger quantities. *Vinca minor* does not appear in classic toxicological handbooks because these discoveries are fairly recent. Poisoning may be caused by overdosage or accidental substitution for another medicine. Symptoms are marked lowering of the blood pressure and ensuing circulatory disorders. There are no known cases of fatal poisoning in animals. Listlessness and digestive disorders have been reported in mules and sheep after grazing on the southern European species *Vinca major* L.

The alkaloids recovered from Lesser Periwinkle are used to lower blood pressure and for certain special purposes in brain therapy. Far more important are the alkaloids vincaleucoblastine and leucocristine obtained from the related *Catharanthus roseus* (L.) G. Don. (syn. *Vinca rosea* L.), an ornamental species that is native to Madagascar but now has a worldwide distribution. They are important anti-cancerous medicines.

Lesser Periwinkle is an evergreen perennial with non-flowering, long, thin, prostrate stems that root at the nodes, and short flowering stems that curve upwards. It is a carpeting plant or undershrub, reaching a height of only 10 – 20 cm. The leaves are opposite, elliptical, leathery and glossy dark green. The flowering period is from March until May. The pentamerous, nearly sessile flowers grow singly from the axils of the leaves. The corolla, up to 3 cm in

diameter, is light blue to violet-blue with
wedge-shaped petals that curve inwards.
The ovary is superior. The fruit is
composed of two follicles joined at the
base (1), that split along the ventral
suture. The seeds (3—5 in each follicle)
are cylindrical and relatively large (2).

Swallowwort
Vincetoxicum hirundinaria Medik.

Asclepiadaceae

Vincetoxicum hirundinaria is a thermophilous species with a Eurasian distribution. Although absent in the northernmost parts of Europe its range extends south to north Africa and in Asia to the Altai and Himalayas. It is found in dry woods, often on limestone substrates.

It contains the poisonous mustard glycoside vincetoxin with a sugar component consisting of oleandrose, thevetose and glucose. Vincetoxin is a mixture of many closely related compounds and its characteristics are similar to those of saponins.

Initial symptoms of poisoning are vomiting and diarrhoea, and these properties were once highly valued as a means of 'expelling poisons from the body', which gave rise to the generic name *Vincetoxicum*, meaning 'victory over poison'. Larger quantities, however, cause paralysis of the respiratory centre. Poisoning also causes paralysis in animals, and chronic poisoning may cause inflammation of the kidneys and urinary passages. American literature contains numerous references to farm animals poisoned by Swallowwort (it is naturalized in the U.S.A.) and to the closely related species of *Asclepias* L. native to the U.S.A. Plants of this species contain cardenolids affecting the heart muscle and sometimes also vincetoxin. Certain related African species of the genus *Vincetoxicum* cause severe poisoning in horses, cattle and sheep accompanied by motor paralysis among other symptoms. In Europe, Swallowwort is virtually no longer used in medicine or as a home remedy.

This perennial, occasionally twining herb reaches a height of more than 1 m. The rhizome is knobbly. The leaves are opposite or in whorls of three, and are heart-shaped-lanceolate with the margin entire. They exhibit marked variability in shape depending on the locality. The flowering period is from May until August. The flowers are greenish white or yellowish white, pentamerous and bell-shaped (1). They are arranged in long-stalked, compact cymes. The fruit consists of two shuttle-like follicles, rounded at the base, pointed at the tip, and measuring 5−7 cm in length (2). The seeds, approximately 0.5 cm long, are flat and ovoid with sharp edges and a silky pappus.

1

2

White Mistletoe
Viscum album L.

Loranthaceae

The genus *Viscum* L. includes approximately 70 semiparasitic species found principally in the tropical and sub-tropical regions of Africa; only a few grow in Asia, northern Australia and Europe. The species *V. album,* which is widely distributed in Eurasia, grows as a semipara- site mainly on deciduous trees. Sometimes it is divided into and classi- fied as separate taxons according to the host on which it lives, for example, the species that grows on conifers is *V. laxum* Boiss. et Reuter, the Common Mistletoe. Recently, the pharmaceutical industry has been exhibiting greater interest in mistletoe.

The plant contains extremely poisonous lectins and peptidic toxins: viscotoxin A_2, A_3 and B, composed of 46 aminoacids. Lectins cause agglutination of red blood corpuscles and have a negative effect on the blood count. That is why, when tea from mistletoe is used as a home remedy for high blood pressure and sclerosis, a person's health may be seriously damaged as a result of anaemia and accom- panying disorders of the body metabolism. Animals cannot be poi- soned by mistletoe because it grows beyond their reach. Birds feed on the berries without harm.

In medicine mistletoe is used in pharmaceutical preparations for lowering high blood pressure and as a cytostatic. It was found that lectins applied in the form of injections may have a beneficial effect in treating inoperable tumours. Treatment of arthritis has also met with positive results.

Mistletoe is also a traditional Christmas decoration.

Mistletoe is an evergreen plant that grows mainly on the branches of deciduous trees. Its roots, called haustoria (1), penetrate the wood, thereby providing the plant with a firm anchorage in the treetop and also with food, which they absorb from the host's conductive tissues. White Mistletoe has a slow growth rate and forms globose clumps about 1 m in diameter. The yellow-green stems, which seemingly branch by forking, are fragile. The thick leathery longish-ovate (approximately 4 by 1.5 cm) leaves have an entire margin and are opposite and nearly sessile. The flowers, produced in March, are monoecious and grow from the axils of the branches. The male flowers (2), larger

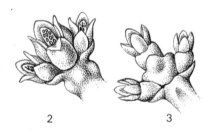

2   3

than the female flowers, are composed of four joined perianth segments and four stamens. The pollen falls from the anthers through minute pores. The female flowers (3), likewise with joined perianth segments, have an inferior ovary and wide stigma. The fruit is a white globose false berry with a sticky pericarp.

1

USEFUL PLANT POISONS

The heading of this brief chapter is only seemingly contradictory for there is no denying the fact that the poisonous substances found in plants also have a positive value. Firstly, they do not harm the plants but definitely serve a biological function. They are not just useless, waste products of metabolism; many are recycled and have a positive effect on the metabolism. They also have a certain defensive function, protecting the plant against natural enemies and pests as well as against grazing animals. Even though they are not vital to the life of the plant this does not necessarily mean that they are of no use to it.

Plant poisons are perhaps most useful to man in medicine, where they are used to treat a wide variety of symptoms and after-effects of disease. One who contributed much to the use of plant poisons in therapy in the second half of the eighteenth century was the prominent Viennese physician Anton Stoerck; one of the species of aconite (plants of the buttercup family, most of which are poisonous) was named after him: *Aconitum stoerckianum* RCHB. The fact that man debased the great ethical value of toxic substances in plants is neither the fault of the poisonous substances nor of the plants in which they are found. Most, as a matter of fact, are lovely plants that have proved useful to man in many ways.

Natives knew of the effects of plant poisons long ago and used them for their own benefit as well as to kill their enemies. Poisoned spears and arrows were not only intended for hunting and obtaining food but also for warfare. Some such poisons with hypnotic properties are even used nowadays in game reserves and zoos to put large animals to sleep (the poison is placed in a special cartridge and shot from a gun) to make handling and transporting them easier.

Poisons of plant origin, e.g. Sea Onion (see *Urginea maritima*) play an important role in the control of rodents such as black and brown rats. It is said that these extraordinarily clever and superbly organized animals deprive man of a third of his food. The control of their numbers is therefore imperative and plant poisons with selective toxicity are eminently suitable for this purpose because they are not harmful to man.

Some poisonous substances of plant origin are of indisputable importance to the further development of the biological sciences as aids for investigating biological processes in the living organism and, if so desired, for influencing these processes. One example is the alkaloid colchicine (see *Colchicum autumnale*). It is one of the most violent poisons for man but not for plants. With colchicine it is possible to change the genetic make-up of plants and produce polyploid organisms (by multiplying the number of chromosomes). These new, polyploid plants are unusually large as a rule and have new, commercially important properties, which also increases the breeding potential of many useful plants such as forage grasses, cereal grasses and vegetables. The use of colchicine for genetic purposes dates from the 1940s and is linked with the names of the world-famous geneticists A. P. Dustin, A. F. Blakeslee and A. G. Avery.

Last, but not least, one cannot but take note of the fact that the poisonous alkaloid caffeine found in coffee (*Coffea arabica* L. — Rubiaceae), tea (*Camellia sinensis* (L.) O. Kuntze — Theaceae), cola seeds (*Cola acuminata* (Pal. Beauv.) Schott et Endl. — Sterculiaceae) and the leaves of maté (*Ilex paraguariensis* St. Hil. — Aquifoliaceae) is an excellent stimulant and effective ingredient of popular beverages. The alkaloid theobromine, found in cocoa and chocolate (*Theobroma cacao* L. — Sterculiaceae) likewise has a refreshing and invigorating effect.

PLANT POISONING

The causes of plant poisoning are many and varied and can be divided into two groups: intentional (criminal) and unintentional. There is no need to discuss the first. Unintentional plant poisoning, however, is generally due to ignorance of the actual effect of the poisonous compounds in the plant. Often even adults, let alone children, have no idea of how dangerous poisonous plants can be. Plant poisoning can be avoided only by the perseverance of doctors, pharmacists, health personnel, etc. in acquainting the public with the dangers of the various offending plants. Children should begin to be taught of the dangers from their earliest years, in a manner suitable to their age level.

A second cause of unintentional poisoning is self-treatment, when people try to treat themselves with plants after hearing or reading about the various beneficial properties. Cases of poisoning caused by dangerous 'experimenting' with plants as a home remedy are not uncommon. Here, too, teaching the public is the only means of prevention.

Underestimation of the effect of certain medicinal plants or the medicines derived from them also can result in unintentional poisoning, particularly when a patient increases the dosage from that prescribed by the doctor. This can lead to dangerous cases of poisoning.

The fourth, and least common cause of accidental poisoning is a mistake on the part of the doctor or pharmacist in prescribing and dispensing the medicine.

POISONOUS SUBSTANCES IN PLANTS

Poisonous substances found in plants may be divided according to their chemical composition and arranged in the order of their proportion and their importance in cases of plant poisoning. Heading the list are two large groups of substances of specific chemical composition: alkaloids and glycosides. Both figure in the descriptions of most of the poisonous plants in the illustrated section of this book.

Alkaloids are a relatively large non-uniform group of organic substances found, according to current knowledge, in approximately 4000 species of plants belonging to various genera and families. Some families of higher plants (e. g. Apocynaceae, Asclepiadaceae, Berberidaceae, Loganiaceae, Papaveraceae, Ranunculaceae, Rubiaceae and Solanaceae) are very rich in alkaloids but some families have none whatsoever, e. g. Rosaceae and Labiatae. Alkaloids are also products of metabolism in certain lower plants. They are organic substances, have alkaline properties, contain nitrogen and generally exert a marked physiological effect on the animal. In plants, they generally occur as complex compounds, as salts of organic acids, rather than in pure form. Pure alkaloids are usually bitter crystalline substances that are both odourless and colourless. Their names are generally derived from the Latin names of plants from which they were isolated. Rarely does a plant contain only one alkaloid; usually it contains a group of chemically related ones. They generally occur in all plant organs, but the highest concentration is chiefly in the roots, bark, leaves and seeds. The concentration also varies, ranging from a fraction of a per cent to several per cent, depending on the stage of development of the respective plant.

More than 3000 alkaloids are known to modern science. The first, the basic alkaloid from opium, morphine, was isolated in 1805 by Friedrich Wilhelm Adam Sertürner (1783—1841).

Glycosides are relatively complex chemical substances of plant origin. They consist of a sugar portion (glucose, rhamnose, galactose, etc.) and a non-sugar portion or aglycone, and they break down into these two separate components on hydrolysis, usually by the action of specific enzymes. Glycosides generally have a pronounced physiological action and are poisonous to animals and humans. They are the product of special metabolic processes in plants, and their concentration in the various plant organs varies in accordance with the age of the plant. Glycosides probably serve as a reserve store of energy for plants that can break the glycosidic bond and use the liberated sugar as they need. Most important from the toxicological aspect are the glycosides that affect the heart. These cardiac glycosides are practically indispensable in the treatment of heart diseases but are the most frequent cause of poisoning due to improper dosage.

Saponins are natural plant substances chemically very like the glycosides. They are distinguished by the fact that they form a soapy foam when dissolved in water and that they destroy red blood corpuscles on direct contact. Some are extremely poisonous (see *Paris quadrifolia, Agrostemma githago*).

Essential oils are a rich mixture of organic compounds, mostly terpenes and sesquiterpenes. They are of oily consistency, practically insoluble in water and readily become resinous when exposed to air. They generally have a pleasant fragrance. They occur in special tissues or in glandular hairs and papillae on the surface of plants. The significance of essential oils in the life of plants has not been fully clarified to date. It appears that besides their physico-chemical function (as a form of protection against excessive evaporation) they also serve a biological function, by attracting pollinators or by repelling animals to prevent grazing. Essential oils accumulate mainly in the flowers and fruits, although leaves and bark also have a high concentration. In some plants, the greatest concentration of essential oils is in the rhizomes and roots. Besides their useful properties — they act as disinfectants and expectorants in diseases of the upper respiratory passages, aid digestion, relieve flatulence, and the like (in therapeutic doses) — they also have certain toxic properties. Many essential oils have an irritant action on the skin and mucous membranes and cause very persistent inflammation. Some essential oils, taken internally, cause severe inflammation of the digestive tract and kidneys, including the urinary passages, while others cause congestion of the pelvic organs and abortion.

Besides the main groups of toxicologically important substances, toxic products are to be found, though in smaller numbers, in other chemical types of plant metabolites. This, of course, does not mean they are any less important from the toxicological aspect. Suffice it to call attention to certain extremely poisonous peptides and proteins such as ricin (see *Ricinus communis*) and crotin (see *Croton tiglium*).

THE MANY FACTORS THAT AFFECT
THE TOXICITY OF PLANTS

If we examine one species of poisonous plant we will find that its toxicity and thus the danger it poses to man and animals is extremely variable. It varies according to the age of the plant, the soil and climatic conditions of the site where it grows, the daily rhythm, or rather the varying concentration of metabolites during the course of the day, and the individual genetical-physiological character of the respective plant. The following examples will serve to illustrate this more clearly.

The age of the plant and different concentration of constituents in the various plant organs are evident chiefly in annual and biennial species; in perennials this factor is not so marked. The seeds of Thornapple (see *Datura stramonium*) contain 0.3—0.5 per cent of alkaloids by weight. In seedlings germinating from these seeds and in young plants, the concentration of alkaloids is about ten times less. Only in plants that are starting to form flower buds does the concentration of alkaloids begin to rise. It increases mainly in the leaves and during the flowering period reaches the level of 0.5—0.7 per cent. Such concentrations may be found also in green capsules that carry on the process of photosynthesis whereas the unripe seeds within the capsules contain only traces of alkaloids. As the capsules and seeds ripen, this ratio is reversed. The dry split capsules have a very low concentration, whereas the ripe seeds contain from 0.3—0.5 per cent of tropane alkaloids. In the case of the perennial Deadly Nightshade, the top parts contain only approximately 0.3 per cent of L-hyoscyamine in spring when they appear, even though the roots from which they grow have up to 1.5 per cent of this alkaloid. Only later, during the flowering period, do the leaves contain from 0.5—1 per cent of L-hyoscyamine: the fruits and seeds contain only slightly less; up to 0.8 per cent.

The concentration of glycosides in foxgloves likewise increases gradually as the plant increases in age, both in the first year of growth when it forms only a basal rosette of leaves, and in the second year when it bears flowering stems. However, this concentration is always lowest in spring. This is ascribed to the low supply of energy at this time of the year. During the growth period there are even fluctuations in the proportion of the various glycosides. Take as an example *Digitalis lanata* Ehrh., which from the beginning of the growth period until summer contains primarily lanatosid A. The concentration of other lanatosids, e. g. lanatosid C, is low. From summer onwards, the same plant produces these lanatosids in completely reverse proportion. In the autumn, the concentration of lanatosid C is higher than that of lanatosid A. Whereas the leaves of foxglove contain a total of approximately 0.3 per cent of glycosides the first year, the leaves of the same plant formed on the flowering stem during the second year of growth contain barely half that amount.

Climatic and soil conditions greatly influence the concentration of toxicologically important substances. Hot dry summer weather generally increases the concentration of alkaloids, glycosides and essential oils. A damp and cool summer reduces the concentration of these substances. This has been proved in practice by comparing the yield of morphine from the Opium Poppy (see *Papaver somniferum*) in various years. The yields from the same variety in the same area differed by as much as 30 per cent. Attempts at introducing certain sub-tropical plants into cultivation in temperate regions showed that the sudden transfer of the respective species to the north was accompanied by a decrease in the production of certain metabolites. For example, oleanders (see *Nerium oleander*) grown for decoration in central Europe had half the concentration of the poisonous glycoside folinerin compared with oleanders growing in the Mediterranean region.

The nutritive value of the soil in which poisonous plants grow also has a definite influence on the concentration of poisonous metabolites. In nitrogen-rich soils, the concentration of alkaloids is higher than in soils that are poor in nitrogen. The composition of the plant community also has a positive or negative effect on the production and concentration of active principles in the plants growing there.

There is a **daily rhythm** to the metabolic process, and the concentration of metabolites, including poisonous substances, varies during the course of the day. As a rule, the concentration of alkaloids, glycosides and essential oils is lowest at night, when the metabolism is more sluggish. The daily fluctuation is most pronounced in the concentration and composition of the essential oils. Daybreak marks the start of photosynthesis and with it a further lowering of the concentration of these metabolites in the plant organs; the plant draws on its store of energy. Between 10 a. m. and 4 p. m. there is a marked increase in the concentration of alkaloids, glycosides, and essential oils in the leaves and the flowers. In the other organs, e. g. roots, fruits and seeds, the effect of the daily rhythm is relatively slight.

The **genetically stable characteristics** of individual species and even of individual plants are the most important influences on the metabolism and its products. These characteristics determine the quantity of poisonous substances the plant is capable of producing.

Some plants have a very high concentration of poisonous substances such as alkaloids, whereas other plants of the same species and population have very little. This natural variability within the species can be expressed by the Gaussian curve. The greatest number of individuals is grouped in the middle with average concentrations, in this case of alkaloids; only a few have markedly lower or markedly higher alkaloid concentrations. The same is true for other substances. This fact is well known to breeders and is the basis of the classic method of selection. By constant selection, along with other methods of breeding, such as hybridization and polyploidization, it is possible to obtain cultivated varieties with minimum or maximum concentrations of the desired substance or substances, including ones that are poisonous to man and animals. Take, for example, the lupin *Lupinus polyphyllus*. The high concentration of alkaloids in this nutritive-rich plant limits its use as fodder. However, by repeated selection of plants with a negligible concentration of these poisonous alkaloids, breeders succeeded in obtaining so-called 'sweet lupins' suitable for use as animal feed.

The reverse process is illustrated by *Digitalis lanata* where the aim was to increase the concentration of a medically valuable glycoside. It has an average concentration of cardiac glycosides of approximately 0.15 per cent of lanatosid C. By selecting from the average population individuals with a high concentration, breeders succeeded in obtaining plants with a concentration of more than 0.5 per cent. Subsequent cross-breeding yielded plants with an average concentration of 0.3 per cent, in other words double the original average concentration. Continued selection and cross-breeding nowadays produces individuals with a concentration of about 1 per cent and cross-breeding of these yields populations with a concentration of more than 0,5 per cent of lanatosid C. In both instances *(Lupinus* and *Digitalis)*, it was through influencing the genes that the desired results were obtained.

FIRST AID FOR PLANT POISONING

Where there is a possibility that serious plant poisoning has occurred, any treatment must be carried out under medical supervision.

It may, however, be difficult to get hold of a doctor right away or to get the victim to a hospital quickly. In such a case first aid must be administered promptly. If possible samples of the suspected plant should be retained for later identification; few people are able to identify plant species and even fewer know which poison each one contains.

The following are general rules for first aid in the event of plant poisoning.

1. Keep calm and keep the patient from getting upset.

2. If the victim has not already been sick, vomiting can be induced by sticking one's finger into his throat (care should be taken not to get bitten). This is in order to get as much poison as possible out of the digestive system. On no account should a salt-water emetic be used as this is potentially toxic in its own right. Vomiting should not be induced if the victim is not fully conscious in case he chokes and inhales fluids into his lungs.

3. Do not forget that in some cases of plant poisoning symptoms may not appear until after several hours. If such a case is suspected (see *Colchicum autumnale, Ricinus communis*) vomiting must be induced promptly.

4. When the victim is vomiting keep his head low and turned to one side to prevent being inhaled any vomit. Try to engage the victim's active cooperation.

5. If activated charcoal is available mix 10 g in a glass of water and give it to the victim to drink. This is a non-toxic adsorbent which will help prevent absorption of the toxin. A second dose may be given together with a mild laxative such as Epsom salts or milk of magnesia.

6. A glass of water or milk may be given to dilute the toxin. Never give anything orally, however, if the victim is not fully conscious, in case it causes choking.

7. Where skin contact with a plant causes a rash and blisters wash the affected areas thoroughly with warm water. Cover with a dry

dressing to prevent excessive scratching and to prevent the blisters becoming infected.

8. It is important for somebody to stay with the victim, while medical aid is being sought, in case he loses consciousness.

9. If the victim loses consciousness he should be placed in the prone position with his head turned to the side. Somebody must stay with him and observe him closely for signs of choking, or in case he has stopped breathing, or his heart has stopped beating.

10. If breathing is failing or cannot be discerned, apply artificial respiration. If there is no detectable pulse apply external cardiac massage. Usually both measures will be required. Resuscitation must be applied immediately it becomes necessary as brain damage can occur very quickly.

PREVENTION OF PLANT POISONING

1. Identify each plant around the home and garden and try to find out if it is poisonous.

2. Store bulbs and seeds out of sight and reach of children.

3. Teach children never to put any plants in their mouths that are not commonly used for food.

4. Only collect mushrooms and plants for eating that you can positively identify.

GLOSSARY

Alkaloid base
— pure alkaloids generally insoluble in water

Analgesic
— a drug that relieves pain

Anamnesis
— the case history of a patient; information about previous diseases; predisposition to disease

Anthelmintic
— a medicine that kills or ejects intestinal worms

Carcinogen
— any substance that produces cancer

Circumpolar distribution
— in the northern hemisphere distribution in the arctic and temperate zones

Cocarcinogen
— any substance that stimulates the latent and minute carcinogenic action of other substances to such a degree that they produce cancer

Cucurbitacines
— poisonous bitter substances occurring in the Cucurbitaceae, Simarubaceae and Rutaceae families

Cytology
— the branch of biology dealing with the structure, function, pathology and life history of cells

Cytostatics
— substances checking cell division, generally applied to medicines checking the growth of malignant or benign cells

Cytotoxic effect
— toxic effect on a cell

Dichasium
— a cyme in which two opposite branches arise below each terminal flower

Endemic species
— restricted to a particular and relatively small region

Furocoumarins
— coumarin derivatives found mainly in plants of the parsley (Umbelliferae) family and rue (Rutaceae) family; they increase the sensitivity of the skin to ultraviolet radiation and may be the cause of certain skin diseases

Galenicals
— medicines prepared from vegetable drugs, e. g. tinctures, extracts, teas, ointments, etc.

Glume
— either of the two empty sterile bracts at the base of a grass spikelet (Gramineae)

Heart failure
— inability of the heart muscle to compensate for the effect of a poison

Heterophylly
— growing leaves of different forms on the same stem or plant

Homeopathy
— a system of medical treatment established by the German physician Dr. Samuel Hahnemann (1755—1843) and based on the theory that certain diseases can be cured by giving very small doses of drugs which in a healthy person and in large doses would produce symptoms like those of the disease, as opposed to allopathy, the general practice of medicine today, which is the treatment of disease by remedies that produce effects different from or opposite to those produced by the disease

Homeopathic drugs
— remedies in which the medicinal substance is greatly diluted, generally ten times (1:10) or 100 times (1:100)

Hypanthium
— a ring or cup around the ovary, usually formed by the union of the lower parts of the calyx, corolla and stamens

Indusium
— a membranous outgrowth of the leaf epidermis in certain ferns, covering the sporangia

Lemma
— the outer or lower of the two bracts or scales enclosing the flower of a grass (Gramineae)

Locular
— consisting of cavities separated by partitions

Necrotic
— dying or decaying tissue
Obsolete
— no longer in use or practice; discarded; out-of-date
Parasympathetic nerves
— part of the autonomic nervous system with an action opposite to that of the sympathetic nerves
Peloric flower
— a seemingly terminal, regular flower in a plant with irregular (zygomorphic) flowers
Photosensitive symptoms
— pathological symptoms caused by exposure to radiant energy, e. g. sunlight
Pinnatipartite (leaf)
— simple leaf pinnately divided about two-thirds of the way to the midrib
Pinnatisect (leaf)
— simple leaf pinnately divided about three-quarters or more of the way to the midrib
Revulsants
— medicines with a strong irritant action on the skin that diminish internal pain caused by a morbid condition in another part of the body, e. g. rheumatism, and partially improve it.
Sclerenchymatic tissue
— plant tissue of uniform thick-walled, dead cells; mechanical tissue that adds strength to an organ
Sorus
— a cluster of spore cases on the undersurface of a fern frond
Sub-lethal dose
— not quite lethal; one that is insufficient to cause death
Tachycardia
— an abnormally fast heartbeat
Therapeutic dose
— curative dose
Tracheotomy
— surgical incision in the trachea for making an artificial breathing hole to prevent suffocation
Triterpenoids
— natural substances with glycosidic or saponin structure common in higher plants
Urolith
— a calculus or stone in the urinary tract

INDEX

Page numbers in *italics* refer to illustrations.